GEOLOGY OF THE DULUTH GABBRO COMPLEX
NEAR DULUTH, MINNESOTA

UNIVERSITY OF MINNESOTA

MINNESOTA GEOLOGICAL SURVEY

PAUL K. SIMS, DIRECTOR

BULLETIN 44

Geology of the Duluth Gabbro Complex near Duluth, Minnesota

BY

RICHARD B. TAYLOR

MINNEAPOLIS · 1964

THE UNIVERSITY OF MINNESOTA PRESS

PRINTED IN THE UNITED STATES OF AMERICA AT
THE LUND PRESS, INC., MINNEAPOLIS

Library of Congress Catalog Card Number: A64-7077

PUBLISHED IN GREAT BRITAIN, INDIA, AND PAKISTAN BY THE OXFORD UNIVERSITY PRESS
LONDON, BOMBAY, AND KARACHI

CONTENTS

v

LIST OF FIGURES

PLATE (in pocket)

LIST OF TABLES

ABSTRACT

Multiple intrusions at Duluth, Minnesota, form a rock series that is here called the Duluth Gabbro Complex. Each of the principal rock types transgresses one or more of the older units. The oldest rock, a coarse-grained anorthositic gabbro that was intruded into the Keweenawan flows, makes up the upper part of the complex. It was intruded by basaltic magma of a second period of magmatic activity which formed rocks that commonly are banded, and hence called the layered series. The gabbroic rocks of the layered series as well as the older anorthositic gabbro are cut by intrusive bodies of ferrogranodiorite and granophyre and by late dikes of basalt and aplite.

The lower two-thirds of the complex, the layered series, is composed chiefly of troctolite, olivine gabbro, feldspathic gabbro, and syenogabbro. About 15,000 feet of layered rocks is exposed, locally with rhythmic banding, fluxion structure, and gravity stratification demonstrating bottom accumulation by crystallization under conditions of active magma circulation. A series of samples collected from bottom to top of the layered series shows only limited development of cryptic layering. This lack of cryptic layering may be explained as the result of periodic renewal of magma in the crystallizing chamber or by multiple small intrusions.

Cross-cutting relations between the different types of gabbro in the layered series show that the mass originated by multiple intrusion. The lack of chilling effects indicates that the successive intrusions were not greatly separated in time. Near the top of the series a transition exists from gabbro to syenogabbro, and a similar transition may exist from syenogabbro to ferrogranodiorite.

The rock series is similar in many respects to that of the Skaergaard Intrusion, but there are important differences that can be explained by dissimilar tectonic history. The poor development of cryptic layering and the absence of ferrogabbro at Duluth, in contrast to their remarkable development in the Skaergaard Intrusion, can be explained by differing tectonic stability. The Skaergaard magma apparently crystallized in a chamber under stable conditions, whereas the Duluth magma seems to have crystallized in an environment of tectonic instability manifested by multiple intrusions of magma.

The various rocks of the Duluth Gabbro Complex can be explained by crystallization-differentiation of basaltic magma, although the origin of some, such as the anorthositic gabbro and intrusive peridotite, is puzzling. The rocks of the layered series probably were derived from a basaltic magma approaching the composition of analyzed late basalt dikes. Compared with the analyses of "marginal olivine gabbro" from the Skaergaard Intrusion, the Duluth parent magma seems to have been notably richer in K_2O, TiO_2, MnO, and P_2O_5.

The Duluth Gabbro Complex is an immense sill-like mass that extends for 150 miles northeast from Duluth, and relations in other parts may differ from those at Duluth.

GEOLOGY OF THE DULUTH GABBRO COMPLEX
NEAR DULUTH, MINNESOTA

1. INTRODUCTION

STATEMENT OF PROBLEM

The Duluth Gabbro Complex of northeastern Minnesota is one of the largest masses commonly included among the stratiform basic intrusions. Earlier studies of the Duluth Gabbro by Grout (1918a,b,c,d) contributed some concepts that have been basic to the study of these igneous bodies. A fundamental one is that convection in the crystallizing magma is instrumental in developing the layering or banding that gives them their stratiform character. This concept has been discussed, modified, and elaborated by Hess (1938), Wager and Deer (1939), Wahl (1946), and Cornwall (1951). In particular, the investigations (Wager and Deer, 1939; Wager and Mitchell, 1951) on the Skaergaard Intrusion in East Greenland have stimulated interest in the mechanisms of crystallization-differentiation as interpreted from studies of the composition trends of minerals, such as the feldspar, pyroxene, and olivine, as well as the distribution of the trace elements.

Unlike the studies of the Skaergaard Intrusion, which demonstrated progressive changes from bottom to top of the stratiform mass, published papers on the Duluth Gabbro have suggested little compositional variation within the several mineral series present, and have strongly emphasized two rock types—gabbro and "red rock" or granite. The present investigation was undertaken, therefore, as a restudy of the gabbro at Duluth with the main objectives of preparing a geologic map of the bedrock and of pursuing mineralogical and chemical studies to elucidate the origin of the rocks.

LOCATION

The Duluth Gabbro Complex makes a crescent-shaped outcrop in St. Louis, Lake, and Cook counties, extending from Duluth to a point near Hovland (Fig. 1), a distance of approximately 150 miles. It has a maximum width of 30 miles in Lake County. The mapped area (Pl. 1) extends 15 miles northward from the southernmost gabbro exposures, covers a maximum width of 12 miles, and includes most of the city of Duluth (see Fig. 1).

PREVIOUS WORK

Studies on the Duluth Gabbro date back to a publication by Kloos (1871). Early workers for the Geological and Natural History Survey of Minnesota (Bayley, 1893, 1895; Elftman, 1895, 1898; Grant, 1889, 1899; Wadsworth, 1887; A. N. Winchell, 1900; N. H. Winchell, 1880,

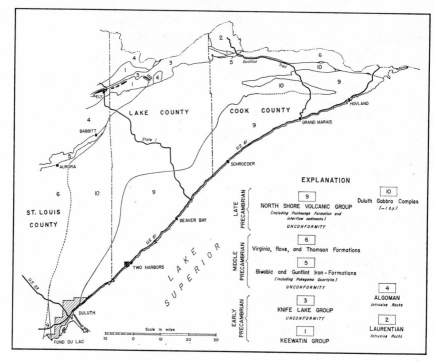

FIGURE 1.—Map of northeastern Minnesota, showing generalized geology.
(Modified from Goldich and others, 1961, pl. 1.)

1885, 1899, 1900) established many of the rock types. The structure of
the region was explored (Irving, 1883; Van Hise and Leith, 1909, 1911;
Leith, Lund and Leith, 1935; Hotchkiss, 1923; Aldrich, 1929) and the
economic possibilities were investigated (Broderick, 1917, 1918; Grout,
1926, 1949–50; Irving, 1883; Nebel, 1919; Schwartz and Davidson, 1952;
N. H. Winchell and H. V. Winchell, 1891; Zapffe, 1912). Grout (1918a–
f) has been the principal contributor to our knowledge of the complex,
and Schwartz (1944, 1949) has summarized much information on the
Duluth area.

Some of the results of the present investigation have been presented
in preliminary papers (Taylor, 1956; Goldich, Taylor, and Lucia, 1956).
A brief summary is also given in Bulletin 41 of the Minnesota Geological Survey, *The Precambrian Geology and Geochronology of Minnesota* (Goldich, Nier, Baadsgaard, Hoffman, and Krueger, 1961).

ACKNOWLEDGMENTS

The problem was suggested by S. S. Goldich, and I am indebted to
him for help in the field and laboratory studies and in the preparation

of this manuscript. G. M. Schwartz, J. W. Gruner, and P. K. Sims critically read the manuscript. All the chemical work was done in the Rock Analysis Laboratory of the University of Minnesota. Robert Heller provided office space at the University of Minnesota, Duluth, during the field seasons. Considerable use was made of field notes, thin sections, and specimens from Grout's earlier work. Able assistance in the field was given in 1953 by F. J. Lucia and in 1954 by H. M. Gehman, Jr. The project was made possible by the financial support of the Minnesota Geological Survey and a Fellowship of the National Science Foundation.

2. GEOLOGIC SETTING

GENERAL STATEMENT

The Duluth Gabbro Complex is a sill-like igneous body dominantly gabbroic in composition on the northwest limb of the Lake Superior geosyncline. It dips southeast, like the overlying Keweenawan lava flows, under the lake. If one travels northward from Duluth along the base of the gabbro, the underlying rocks include Keweenawan flows, the Thomson Formation, the Biwabik and Virginia formations of the east Mesabi Range, Algoman granitic rocks of the Giant's Range, Keewatin Greenstone, the Knife Lake Group, the Gunflint Iron-Formation, and the Rove Slate (Fig. 1). The apparent transgression is explained by Grout (1918a) as the result of intrusion along an erosion surface on which the Keweenawan rocks had been laid down.

The gabbro was intruded approximately one billion years ago and its chronological position is shown in the Precambrian succession of northeastern Minnesota in Table 1 (Goldich and others, 1961). Brief descriptions of the formations in the Duluth region are given here; for more detailed data the reader is referred to Bulletin 41 of the Minnesota Geological Survey and to the older publications listed in the references.

THOMSON FORMATION

The Thomson Formation, composed of interbedded graywacke and slate, crops out in the western part of the area (Pl. 1). The dark-gray graywacke is fine- to coarse-grained, poorly sorted, and contains angular grains of quartz, feldspar, and rock fragments in a matrix of quartz, chlorite, and sericite. The black slate has well-developed flow cleavage and is composed largely of sericite and quartz, with lesser amounts of chlorite, carbonate, feldspar, leucoxene, and magnetite. Near Duluth the formation strikes roughly eastward at about a 45° angle to the trend of the Lake Superior geosyncline. The Keweenawan rocks rest with angular unconformity on the truncated Thomson Formation, as can be seen in exposures near the Grandview golf course.

The Thomson Formation is the oldest unit mapped (Pl. 1). It was tentatively correlated by the Minnesota Geological Survey (Grout, Gruner, Schwartz, and Thiel, 1951, p. 1021) with the Knife Lake Group. The recent geochronologic studies, however, suggest that the Thomson Formation is much younger than the Knife Lake Group and probably is of Huronian age (Table 1).

4

TABLE 1. STRATIGRAPHIC SUCCESSION OF THE PRECAMBRIAN ROCKS OF NORTHEASTERN MINNESOTA
(modified from Goldich and others, 1961; italicized units crop out in the Duluth area)

Era	Period-System	Major Sequence	Formation	Intrusive Rocks
			. . . . unconformity	
(0.6 b.y.)			Hinckley Sandstone	
			Fond du Lac Sandstone	
			. . . . unconformity	
(1.1 b.y.) Late Precambrian	Keweenawan	*North Shore Volcanic Group*	undivided	*Duluth Complex, sills at Duluth,* Beaver Bay Complex, Logan intrusives
			Puckwunge Formation	
			. . . . unconformity	
(1.7 b.y.)			Virginia Argillite = Rove = *Thomson*	
Middle Precambrian	Huronian	Animikie Group	Biwabik Iron-Formation = Gunflint	
			Pokegama Quartzite	
			. . . . unconformity	Algoman granitic rocks
(2.5 b.y.)	Timiskamian	Knife Lake Group	undivided	
			. . . . unconformity	Laurentian granitic rocks
(? b.y.)			Soudan Iron-Formation	
Early Precambrian	Ontarian	Keewatin Group	Ely Greenstone	
		Coutchiching (?)	undivided	

5

PUCKWUNGE FORMATION

The Puckwunge Formation is a buff to gray sandstone. Two outcrops in the southwestern part of the area (Pl. 1), just north of the Grand-view golf course, are well-indurated sandstone or quartzite overlain by a Keweenawan lava flow. According to Schwartz (1949, p. 22) the conglomerate at the base of the Puckwunge Formation was once exposed in this area, but at present is covered with slumped material. The conglomerate is well exposed in the bed of the St. Louis River in Jay Cooke State Park, a few miles southwest of the mapped area.

NORTH SHORE VOLCANIC GROUP

The flows and minor interflow sediments that constitute the North Shore Volcanic Group along the north shore of Lake Superior extending from Duluth to Two Harbors have been described in detail by Sandberg (1938). The extrusive rocks, including the interflow fragmental rocks, are about 21,000 feet thick. Felsites make up nearly 10 per cent of this thickness, and interflow sediments—chiefly sandstone—just over 1 per cent; most of the flows are basalt. A recent estimate (Grout, Gruner, Schwartz and Thiel, 1951, p. 1054) of the total thickness of flows on the north shore of Lake Superior is 30,000 feet. Earlier measurements by Sandberg indicate a possible maximum thickness of 2500 feet of basalt flows beneath the gabbro at Duluth. This thickness decreases rapidly to the north as the gabbro transgresses over successively older rocks. The dip of the flows beneath and above the gabbro at Duluth is virtually the same, approximately 15°E., and suggests a concordant intrusion, but the concordancy at best is local and is more apparent than real.

The interflow sediments are chiefly gray to buff or pink, medium-grained sandstones. They are thinly laminated and generally crossbedded. The units are thin, composed largely of the disintegration products of flows. The thickest sandstone unit is 114 feet thick (Sandberg, 1938, p. 810) and is well exposed along the lake shore in Lief Erickson Park. The rough amygdaloidal tops of some of the flows acted as traps for sediments washed over them, and are now complex mixtures of clastic and flow materials.

DULUTH GABBRO COMPLEX

The North Shore volcanics are the surface extrusions of a period of igneous activity that culminated in the intrusion of enormous volumes of gabbroic magma in Keweenawan time. A series of rocks, closely related in composition and in distribution, formed through differentiation of basaltic parent magma. These rocks show cross-cutting relations, chilled border phases, and intimate structural relations that can be explained only as the results of multiple intrusion. The greater part of these intrusive rocks are here referred to as the Duluth Gabbro Complex. Lesser bodies, as for example the Endion sill (Schwartz and Sandberg, 1940; Ernst, 1961), may be closely related, but because they are smaller igneous bodies of rather distinctive character, they are for the present excluded from the Duluth Gabbro Complex.

The duration of the period of igneous activity that resulted in the flows and the intrusive rocks of the Duluth region is not known. Apparently the activity had died out before deposition of the Fond du Lac Formation. These gray to red interbedded sandstones and shales do not occur in the mapped area but crop out just south at Fond du Lac (Fig. 1). The Fond du Lac Formation is assigned to the Upper Keweenawan (Table 1).

PLEISTOCENE DEPOSITS

Glacial deposits cover to varying depths the greater part of the bedrock of the Duluth region. They include till from the Superior lobe and clays, sand, and gravel deposits of glacial Lake Duluth. The Pleistocene deposits were not mapped or studied in this investigation. They have been discussed briefly, however, by Schwartz (1949).

3. DULUTH GABBRO COMPLEX

GENERAL STATEMENT

In the Duluth area, the various gabbros, ferrogranodiorite, and granophyre are referred to collectively as the Duluth Gabbro Complex. The gabbroic rocks were formed in two major periods of intrusion that were sufficiently separated in time for the older gabbro to have become cold before intrusion of the younger gabbro. Grout (1918b, p. 627) recognized the two gabbros and referred to the older as feldspathic gabbro and to the younger as banded gabbro. The rocks of the first period have been mapped here as anorthositic gabbro. The rocks of the second period are more normal gabbroic rocks in their content of mafic minerals, compared with the anorthositic gabbro. These rocks, formed by several intrusions, are characterized by a distinct layering and are referred to as the layered series. The various intrusive bodies can be distinguished locally on the basis of cross-cutting relations, but the lack of chilling effects at contacts indicates that they were formed at closely spaced intervals. Because of lithologic similarity, the individual intrusive bodies of the layered series were not mapped separately in the Duluth area except for a small body near Bardon Peak, which can be readily distinguished in the field (Pl. 1). Closely related to gabbros of the layered series are intrusive bodies of granodioritic and granitic composition. The granodiorite is a high-iron, low-silica, pyroxene-bearing rock that herein is called a ferrogranodiorite. The silicic intrusions are granophyres, ranging from adamellite to granite in composition, and called "red rock" in the earlier literature. The rock types are described in the following sections; their origins are considered later.

Age determinations (Goldich and others, 1961) on the extrusive and intrusive igneous rocks of the North Shore region define the Keweenawan activity as approximately 1.1 b.y. in age. A series of samples from the gabbro and its related differentiates gave ages ranging from 1.06 to 1.2 b.y., and recrystallized or heated rocks from formations near the gabbro contact gave similar ages. The absolute ages for the gabbro and the other major events of the Precambrian of northeastern Minnesota are summarized in Table 1.

ANORTHOSITIC GABBRO

General Description. The oldest rock of the Duluth Gabbro Complex is a generally coarse-grained rock containing 75–90 per cent calcic labradorite that crops out in a zone about three miles wide (Pl. 1). It is characterized by abundant inclusions and appears in many outcrops to consist of a jumble of large blocks in a coarse feldspathic matrix. A variety of gabbroic types can be distinguished among the blocks by differences in fabric and in proportion of minerals (Fig. 2). Inclusions of anorthosite have a maximum diameter of about 25 feet, and are composed of more than 95 per cent plagioclase. They resemble closely the anorthosite inclusions in the diabase of the Beaver Bay region to the north (Grout and Schwartz, 1939). They generally are well rounded, perhaps as a result of mechanical attrition during transport. The anorthositic gabbro was intruded as a crystal mush, and most of the inclusions probably represent early solid phases subsequently broken up, incorporated into the magma, and moved with it to their present position.

Contacts. The upper contact of the anorthositic gabbro is covered in most places, but is well exposed at two localities, where it dips at a low angle roughly concordant with the overlying basalt flows. A contact exposed behind Villa Scholastica shows coarse feldspathic gabbro that intruded and broke up basalt flows. Small dikes of the gabbro in the flows show little sign of chilling; feldspar crystals an inch in length occur in dikes only a few inches wide. The basalt flow is recrystallized adjacent to the gabbro to a granoblastic texture, and contains many veinlets of dark minerals, chiefly amphibole, that appear related to the gabbro. Many inclusions of basalt hornfels occur in the gabbro. In Section 30, T.50N., R.14W., near the WFTV television station, recrystallized basalt is intruded by a mafic phase of the anorthositic gabbro. This gabbro is finer grained than at Villa Scholastica and apophyses in the flows are very fine-grained, suggesting chilling.

The nature of the original basal contact of the anorthositic gabbro is not known because the lower part of the unit is cut out by the younger layered gabbro or by the ferrogranodiorite along Coffee Creek. The contact with these younger rocks is complex and generally poorly exposed; the north-trending contact shown on Plate 1 is inferred. The contact with the layered series can be located more precisely along the southern margin. Along Miller Creek approximately 1500 feet south of Skyline Drive the younger gabbro is chilled adjacent to the anorthositic gabbro, indicating that the anorthositic gabbro had cooled before the intrusion of the layered series. This contact zone was the locus of emplacement of dikes and small irregular-shaped intrusive bodies of granophyre. The contact of layered series gabbro with the anorthositic gabbro northeast of Keene Creek that roughly parallels the creek is not exposed, but can be located within a few feet. Many inclusions of anorthositic gabbro occur in the younger gabbro, and large inclusions occur as far as two miles from the contact. Apparently widely spaced joints in the massive anorthositic gabbro caused it to break up into

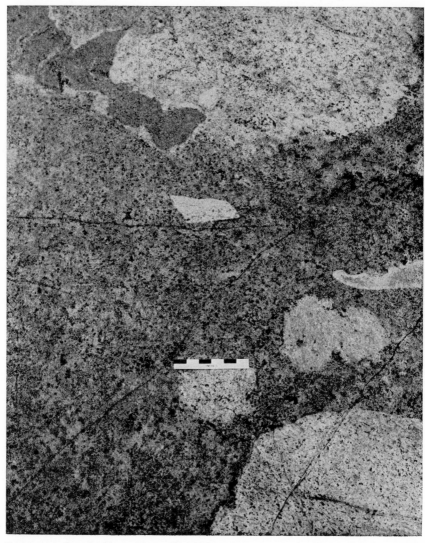

FIGURE 2.—Anorthositic gabbro. Glaciated outcrop of anorthositic gabbro near 27th Avenue West and 12th Street; coarse-grained anorthositic gabbro surrounds cognate inclusions which vary in composition from melanocratic pyroxene gabbro to anorthosite. (Six-inch ruler in photo indicates scale.)

large pieces, which were incorporated in the younger gabbro; these are sufficiently different from the rocks of the layered series to be recognizable in the field.

Internal Structure. The anorthositic gabbro does not contain mappable internal structures and its most conspicuous feature is the many inclusions that give the rock the appearance of an igneous breccia. This breccia is especially well developed in the rocks exposed southwest of 27th Avenue and along Skyline Drive southwest of its intersection with Haines Road.

Flow structures in the anorthositic gabbro around the inclusions, most of which are cognate, show differential movement. These local flow lines obscure larger structures that may be present. Banded structures such as those that characterize the layered series are lacking.

Petrography. Several textural varieties of the anorthositic gabbro can be distinguished. Most of them are spotted, with poikilitic crystals of titanaugite, magnetite-ilmenite, and less commonly olivine, enclosing labradorite laths. Single augite crystals, up to six inches across, enclose hundreds of feldspar crystals and can be distinguished by their cleavage and schiller structure. Other poikilitic minerals approach the augite in size. Upon weathering, the mafic minerals produce dark-gray stained areas that contrast with the light-gray, plagioclase-rich areas. The plagioclase in these spotted rocks shows little orientation. Other rocks in the anorthositic gabbro have well-developed fluxion structure produced by parallel orientation of feldspar plates. The orientation was caused by movements while the material was a crystal mush. Intersertal magnetite-ilmenite and ophitic augite form a matrix for the feldspar. Table 2 gives the mode of anorthositic gabbro from Skyline Drive above the 57th Avenue quarry. This gabbro has large spots of augite crystals, and is uncommonly rich in olivine.

The plagioclase content of the anorthositic gabbro ranges from about 50 to nearly 100 per cent, and averages about 80 per cent. True anortho-

TABLE 2. MODE (VOLUME PER CENT) OF ANORTHOSITIC GABBRO

	1		1
Plagioclase	69	Serpentine	p
Titanaugite	9	Talc	p
Olivine	12	Chlorite	p
Magnetite-ilmenite	9	Prehnite	p
Apatite	p	Leucoxene	p
Biotite	p	Zoisite	p
Sulfide	p	Hisingerite (?)	p
Uralite	p	Johannsen No.	(2312)

1. Feldspathic olivine gabbro, M3755-1. Skyline Drive on bluff above 57th Avenue West quarry. Average of 6 thin sections. Plagioclase, average composition An_{60}; range in zoned crystals, An_{54-73}. Titanaugite, $gamma = 1.716$; $2V = 46°$. Olivine, $beta = 1.738$; Fa_{41}.

site, with more than 95 per cent plagioclase, occurs only as discrete inclusions. The grain size of the anorthosite varies widely from one piece to another; one crystal of feldspar observed was 14 inches long; other masses have a cataclastic texture and are so fine-grained as to resemble chert. The anorthosite may be massive, show rude banding due to segregation of the minor amounts of dark minerals, or have fluxion structure caused by planar orientation of feldspar. The edges of some inclusions are enriched in augite in coarsely crystalline masses, presumably resulting from additions from the surrounding magma. The plagioclase from the anorthosite ranges in composition from labradorite (An_{55}) to bytownite (An_{75}) in the specimens examined. Augite is the most abundant mafic mineral, but magnetite-ilmenite and olivine may also be present. Alteration minerals generally are sparse, chiefly consisting of serpentine, chlorite, and prehnite.

Gabbro pegmatite occurs as segregations with indefinite boundaries in the anorthositic gabbro unit. Titanaugite and labradorite (about An_{60}) are the most common minerals, and ilmenite, magnetite, biotite, and apatite are common accessories. The minerals are similar in composition to those in the surrounding gabbro. Late stage alteration uralitized the augite, sericitized the edges of some of the plagioclase crystals, and formed small pink crystals of orthoclase perthite. The pegmatitic texture may have resulted from the local accumulation of volatiles that increased rates of diffusion in the magma, and thus increased the grain size. The abandoned quarry at 57th Avenue West shows some of the largest pegmatitic segregations in the anorthositic gabbro. Accompanying them are several unusual veins of augite with minor amounts of ore minerals. These veins have sharp contacts and are as much as six inches wide. The augite crystals are oriented nearly at right angles to the walls, and some extend from wall to wall. Migration of augite-forming material from the partly solidified pegmatite into cracks in the surrounding rock may account for these unusual features, but a hydrothermal origin by replacement cannot be excluded.

The anorthositic gabbro is similar mineralogically to the other gabbros at Duluth. The plagioclase is zoned, generally in the range An_{60-65}; calcic cores in one sample are An_{73}. Normal zoning from a calcic core to a sodic rim is common, and corrosion zoning due to resorption, and oscillatory zoning are also noted. The olivine normally is in small rounded grains, but some is molded around other minerals indicating late crystallization. The common pyroxene is titanaugite that has well-developed schiller structure of ore plates.

THE LAYERED SERIES

General Description. The rocks of the layered series, making up two thirds of the gabbro at Duluth (Pl. 1), were intruded into the anorthositic gabbro. They are characterized by medium grain size, by containing olivine as an important constituent, by having less feldspar than the anorthositic gabbro, and by having primary banding or fluxion structures that show consistent orientation over considerable areas. The banding, fluxion structure, and local gravitational stratification show that the rocks are bottom crystal accumulates similar in origin to the rocks of the Skaergaard Intrusion (Wager and Deer, 1939).

Upper Contact. The upper contact of the layered series with the anorthositic gabbro is complex, and not well exposed. It can be traced with some degree of accuracy in the southern part of the area (Pl. 1). Just north of Keene Creek the contact dips steeply and strikes N.20°W. At the top of the 57th Avenue West quarry a complex apophysis at least 40 feet thick extends into the anorthositic gabbro. The apophysis was emplaced in two stages; the first, a dike about six feet thick, was chilled to a fine-grained basalt by the cold anorthositic gabbro host, but flow lines marked by the orientation of feldspar plates were formed. A later intrusion of olivine gabbro broke the basalt into large blocks, and caused it to be recrystallized to a hornfels. A chemical analysis of a sample of the basalt hornfels collected northwest of the quarry at 57th Avenue West (Table 3) is similar to an older analysis from the quarry itself. The hornfels is characteristically enriched in titania (7 per cent). Earlier, Schwartz (1949, p. 90) interpreted the hornfels to be large inclusions of basalt flow recrystallized by the heat of the anorthositic gabbro. The almost complete lack of inclusions within the anorthositic gabbro and the number of large blocks forming an almost continuous layer at the bottom of the later olivine gabbro intrusion argue against this interpretation.

TABLE 3. CHEMICAL ANALYSES AND MODE OF BASALT HORNFELS

	1	2		1	2
SiO_2	41.31	42.98	S	.10	...
Al_2O_3	12.12	13.09		99.92	100.11
Fe_2O_3	3.52	3.16	C = S	−.04	
FeO	14.57	13.38		99.88	
MgO	6.58	6.44			
CaO	11.07	11.33	*Mode of M3763 (Sample I)*		
Na_2O	2.06	2.22	Labradorite (An_{60})		42
K_2O	.16	.23	Olivine		6
H_2O+	.44	.51	Augite		38
H_2O-	.06	.04	Magnetite-ilmenite		14
CO_2	.05	...	Sulfide		p
TiO_2	7.04	6.52	Uralite		p
P_2O_5	.63	...	Serpentine		p
MnO	.21	.21	Hisingerite		p

1. Basalt hornfels, M3763, northwest of 57th Avenue West quarry. Eileen H. Oslund, analyst.

2. Basalt hornfels, 57th Avenue West quarry. G. Kahn, analyst (Schwartz, 1943, p. 1222).

The mode of the olivine gabbro from the apophysis is given in Table 4 (No. 9); the plagioclase is about An_{61}, and the olivine is Fa_{47}.

About one and a half miles northwest of Skyline Drive the trend of the upper contact changes to N.20°E. Along this contact the gabbro of the layered series contains many inclusions of anorthositic gabbro, two large enough to be mapped (Pl. 1). The mapped inclusions are separated from the main mass of anorthositic gabbro by a thin tongue of chilled gabbro of the layered series.

On Miller Creek the contact zone of the layered series with the anorthositic gabbro is marked by small dikes of chilled basalt that extend into the anorthositic gabbro. Later granophyre intruded this chilled zone, and it contains many basalt inclusions derived from the fine-grained border rock. The exposures on the southeast corner of Sec. 30, T.50N., R.14W. show an igneous breccia of fine- to medium-grained gabbro of the layered series that encloses large blocks of coarse anorthositic gabbro.

North of the intersection of Miller Creek and Skyline Drive, in an area of scattered exposures, the upper contact zone of the layered series is more complex because of the ferrogranodiorite mass (Pl. 1).

The contact zone is not exposed north of Highway 53, but a northward trend for the contact is believed probable (Pl. 1); its position is believed accurate within about a mile. Few outcrops are present in this area, and none show the chilled phase of the layered series.

Lower Contact. The western, basal contact of the layered series trends northward and dips eastward. It transgresses about 2500 feet of basalt flows from the southernmost exposure northward for a distance of about eight miles, and toward the north intrudes the Thomson Formation. The base is not exposed except at the extreme southern end of the gabbro at Bardon Peak, and the contact on Plate 1 is based largely on magnetometer traverses by Schwartz (1944).

Near Bardon Peak the contact strikes about N.10°W. and dips about 45°E. The banded structure has a similar strike, but a smaller angle of dip, from 20° to 30°. The Keweenawan basalt flows beneath the gabbro have been recrystallized to a fine-grained hornfels. The gabbro near the contact is a diabasic olivine gabbro with poikilitic pyroxene enclosing plagioclase and olivine. The rock grades upward to troctolite with gravitational stratification.

Internal Structure. Banded structures with systematic orientation justify the name layered series for this unit. Grout (1918b,c) discussed these structures, distinguishing igneous banding, the alternation of layers with different mineralogic proportions, and fluxion structure, the parallelism of platy or needle-shaped minerals. He concluded that the action of convection currents was necessary to orient the crystals, and that circulatory movements would explain the alternation of mineral-

ogically unlike bands. Wager and Deer (1939) extended this concept
to explain similar structures in the Skaergaard Intrusion and distinguished
three types: (1) rhythmic layering, the type of banding giving nearly
planar surfaces and rhythmically repeated; (2) cryptic layering, the
gradual change in composition of the minerals in the layers; and (3)
igneous lamination, the parallel orientation of the platy minerals.

Rhythmic layering is developed in many parts of the gabbro at Duluth. The banded troctolite of Bardon Peak is well layered, and shows
gravitational stratification. Near Keene Creek along Skyline Drive,
olivine gabbro is similarly layered, with feldspathic and mafic layers
alternating. Some of the mafic layers are enriched in ilmenite, others in
augite and olivine. Along the western edge of Sec. 7, T.50N., R.14W.,
near the Duluth airport, olivine gabbro is well layered.

Rhythmic layering is broken up in Sec. 12, T.49N., R.15W. by the
intrusion of younger gabbro. Several lines of evidence indicate that the
interruption represents intrusion and not slumping. The layering is
sharply broken at contacts with the younger gabbro, though the pres-
ence of curved layers indicates that the rock was soft enough to bend
considerably. Also, the composition of the layered rock in some cases
differs appreciably from the younger gabbro. Finally, the area near
Keene Creek has a few small apophyses of the younger gabbro in the
banded rock, with very slight displacements of the banded material.

Large-scale banding with units tens of feet thick is encountered in
the gabbro. The units are lenticular, and their size and shape probably
were determined by the particular magma movements which led to
their formation. The detailed maps of the titaniferous-magnetite ore
deposits (Broderick, 1917; Grout, 1949–50) emphasize the lenticular
character of such units.

Fluxion structure equivalent to the igneous lamination of Wager and
Deer results from the parallel alinement of plagioclase crystals, usually
flattened parallel to 010, and is another indication of movements in the
magma. The fluxion structure in banded rocks parallels the banding.

Banding in a single outcrop in Sec. 15, T.49N., R.15W., seems to be of
a different type. In this outcrop the grain size of adjacent bands differs.
The coarse bands are somewhat discontinuous and consist of well-foliated
olivine gabbro. The fine bands are gabbro that is richer in olivine and
seems to break across the coarser ones. A few large crystals that occur
in the fine-grained gabbro may be xenocrysts. It is difficult to account
for the alternation in grain size of the bands except by postulating different rates of cooling and nucleation. Possibly the banding is the result of rifting of a nearly solid crystal mush locally affecting a few feet of
rock. It is not possible to trace this banding from one outcrop to
another.

Petrography. Detailed sampling across the layered series along an

TABLE 4. MODES (VOLUME PER CENT) OF GABBROIC ROCKS FROM THE LAYERED SERIES
(Samples 1-8 in order of height in the series)

	1	2	3	4	5	6	7	8	9	10	11	12	13	14
Plagioclase	59	81	50	81	78	45	45	44	60	57	77	30	47	17
Clinopyroxene	32	4	25	p	p	37	26	27	21	1	6	35	31	49
Orthopyroxene		p		4	9	p	8	1	p	p	2	p	8	
Olivine	4	12	20	12	8	7	12	6	9	40	12	9		15
Magnetite	2	2	5	1	2	9	3	2	10	2	2	24	8	18
Apatite	p	p	p	1	1	1	p	1	p	p	1	p	1	p
Biotite	p	p	p	1	2	1	2	1	p	p	p	2	2	1
Sulfides	p	p	p				p	p	p	p	p	p	p	p
Hornblende	p					p		p	p	p	p	p	p	p
Serpentine	1	p	p	p	p	p	1		p					
Talc	p	p			p			p						p
Uralite	2				p		1	2	p	p	p	p	p	p
Chlorite	p	p		p	p		p	5			p	p	p	p
Orthoclase							4	5					3	
Quartz							2	1					p	
Johannsen No.	(2312)	(2312)	(2312)	(2312)	(2312)	(3312)	(2311)	(2311)	(2312)	(2312)	(2312)	(3312)	(2311)	(3312)

p = less than 1 per cent.

1. Diabasic olivine gabbro, G1006. Center Sec. 17, T.50N., R15W.

2. Feldspathic augite troctolite, M3711. NE¼ Sec. 29, T.50N., R.15W.

3. Olivine gabbro, M3716-1. Center N. side, Sec. 27, T.50N., R.15W.

4. Feldspathic hypersthene troctolite, M3716-3. Center N. side, Sec. 27, T.50N., R.15W.

5. Feldspathic olivine norite, M3720. Center S. side, Sec. 26, T.50N., R.15W.

6. Olivine melagabbro, M3725. SE¼ Sec. 25, T.50N., R.15W.

7. Magnetite syenogabbro, M3728. NE¼ Sec. 30, T.50N., R.14W.

8. Microsyenogabbro, G580. Miller Creek SE of Skyline Drive, at contact of layered series and anorthositic gabbro.

9. Olivine gabbro, M3706-6. Top of 57th Avenue quarry, center Sec. 6, T.49N., R.14W.

10. Banded troctolite, M4634. Bardon Peak, on upper tracks of Canadian National Railway, Sec. 34, T.49N., R.15W.

11. Banded feldspathic olivine gabbro, P55G. Rest Point, on Highway 61, center Sec. 14, T.49N., R.15W.

12. Banded magnetite melagabbro, M3771. Keene Creek, SE¼-NW¼ Sec. 12, T.49N., R.15W.

13. Hypersthene-syenogabbro, M3772. Same locality as M3771.

14. Magnetite olivine melagabbro, M3706-p. Dike cutting anorthosite gabbro at 57th Avenue quarry, center Sec. 6, T.49N., R.14W.

TABLE 5. SUMMARY OF MINERALOGIC DATA FOR GABBROIC ROCKS OF THE LAYERED SERIES

No.*	Sample No.	Plagioclase (% Anorthite)		Augite		Hyper-sthene		Olivine	
		Av.	Range	2V	Gamma†	2V	Comp.	Beta†	Comp.
1	G1006	61	55–63	44	1.713			1.734	Fa 39
2	M3711	65	58–65	45				1.738	Fa 41
3	M3716-1	59	54–59	44	1.717			1.743	Fa 43
4	M3716-3	60	54–62			56	Fs 37	1.738	Fa 41
5	M3720	62	54–64			56	Fs 37	1.741	Fa 42
6	M3725	60	56–61	45	1.719	56	Fs 37		
7	M3728	54	50–55	46		53	Fs 43		
8	G580	53	48–55						
9	M3706-6	61	47–63	43	1.716	58	Fs 34	1.751	Fa 47
10	M4634	65	53–67	42	1.716			1.735	Fa 39
11	P55G	60	57–62			58	Fs 34	1.740	Fa 42
12	M3771	61							
13	M3772	62	55–65						
14	M3706-p	58	55–59					1.746	Fa 44

* Numbers correspond with the list of localities and modes for samples in Table 4.
† Indices of refraction are accurate to ±.002.

TABLE 6. MINERALOGIC TRENDS IN ROCKS OF THE LAYERED SERIES ALONG EAST-WEST LINE OF SECTION JUST NORTH OF ENGER TOWER

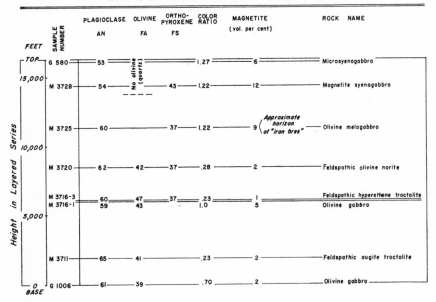

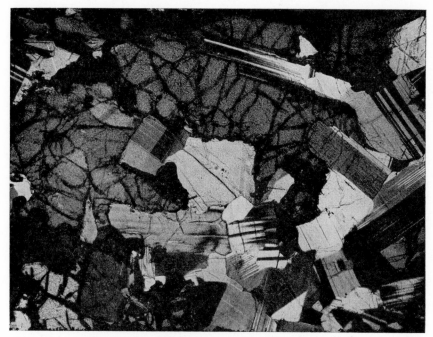

FIGURE 3.—Poikilitic olivine molded around plagioclase laths. This form of olivine is unusual, and indicates crystallization from the interprecipitate liquid. Sample M3716-3. 7½X, crossed nicols.

east-west line just north of Enger Tower was done in an attempt to establish the sequence of rock types and the mineralogic variation within the mass. A preliminary examination of 20 of these samples was made; eight were selected for detailed study (Tables 4, 5, and 6). The lateral variation of rock types along the line of section is too great to establish a regular vertical succession for the layered series in the Duluth area.

The olivine gabbro near the western contact of the layered series with the underlying basalt flows has a diabasic texture and is fine- to medium-grained. Sample G1006 (No. 1, Tables 4 and 5) is from an outcrop of this rock only a few yards from recrystallized basalt flows, near the center of Sec. 17, T.49N., R.15W.; the rock has no layered structure.

Outcrops in Sec. 29, T.50N., R.15W., about 1860 feet stratigraphically above the exposed base of the layered series, are feldspathic olivine gabbro. The rock (M3711, No. 2, Tables 4 and 5) has a poorly developed fluxion structure, no banding, and is medium-grained with rounded olivine and tabular labradorite.

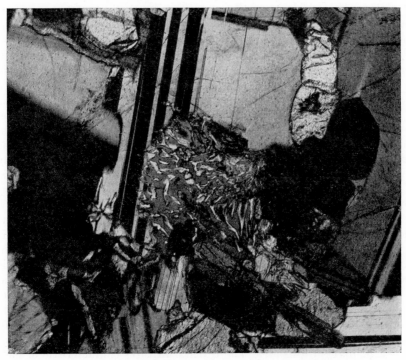

FIGURE 4.—Myrmekitic intergrowth of orthopyroxene and plagioclase. A late magmatic intergrowth crystallized from the interprecipitate liquid.
Sample M3716-3. 115X, crossed nicols.

Along the line of section about two miles east of the basal contact the rocks are more variable in mineralogic proportions and in texture. Augite is more abundant than in the rocks to the west, although troctolite is still an important rock type. Contacts between the different varieties may be sharp, but more commonly are gradational. It was not possible to trace any of the contacts because of a lack of outcrops.

Along the Hermantown Road, in the center near the north line of Sec. 27, T.50N., R.15W.—about 6100 feet above the exposed base of the layered series—an abrupt change in rock type can be observed. At the base of the exposure is a spotted gabbro, (M3716-1, No. 3, Tables 4 and 5) that has 1 to 20cm poikilitic crystals of titanaugite, magnetite-ilmenite, and olivine enclosing plagioclase laths. Olivine in the form of poikilitic crystals (Fig. 3) is rare in other rocks and indicates crystallization from the interprecipitate material surrounding the primary plagioclase crystals that accumulated on the floor of the intrusion. Late-stage intergrowths of magnetite with pyroxene or olivine are common. Armoring of magnetite with a fringe of biotite and wormy intergrowths of orthopyroxene in plagioclase (see Fig. 4) indicate late magmatic activity. The lack of alinement of the plagioclase plates indicates that the rock formed from quiescent magma from which many plagioclase crystals and a few olivine and pyroxene crystals were settling. A half-inch transition layer, rich in biotite, separates the spotted gabbro from a feldspathic troctolite (M3716-3, No. 4, Tables 4 and 5) that has a well-developed fluxion structure.

Feldspathic olivine gabbro, troctolite, and olivine norite are common rock types in the central zone of the layered series. One sample from this zone, sample M3720 (No. 5, Tables 4 and 5), taken from the middle of the south line of Sec. 26, T.50N., R.14W. and stratigraphically about 8400 feet above the base of the layered series, is a feldspathic olivine norite. The rock has a fluxion structure caused by planar orientation of the feldspar plates.

Near the center of Sec. 25, T.50N., R.15W., stratigraphically about 11,300 feet above the base of the layered series, the chief rock type is an olivine melagabbro (M3725, No. 6, Tables 4 and 5) of medium grain that has a fluxion structure. The most abundant mafic mineral in this rock is titanaugite in rounded crystals that only rarely show intersertal texture. The plagioclase is about An_{60} and the plates have a subparallel orientation. The inverted pigeonite has two sets of lamellae in the orthopyroxene host. The magnetite-ilmenite content is high, and lean titaniferous-magnetite ores were reported by Winchell (Winchell and Winchell, 1891) in this area. The textural features characteristic of melanocratic gabbros (Wager, 1953) are shown by this rock. The mafic material crystallizing late from the interprecipitate material forms around the primary precipitate crystals of the same type, and the abundant nuclei do not permit development of the large poikilitic crystals that are found in the rocks with few primary precipitate ferromagnesian minerals. Only apatite is intersertal and does not develop its typical euhedral hexagonal prisms. Segregation by igneous processes of crystal settling with convection currents, perhaps with elutriation-differentiation, probably accounts for the concentration of the magnetite-ilmenite in lenses in the rock.

Sample M3728 (No. 7, Tables 4 and 5) from the NE½ Sec. 30, T.50N., R.14W., about 14,300 feet stratigraphically above the exposed base of the layered series, is a magnetite-rich syenogabbro. The clinopyroxene is a tan titanaugite. Inverted pigeonite has a coarse set of lamellae of augite and a finer set of diopside. Magnetite and inverted pigeonite are commonly intergrown, and the relations suggest late-stage replacement of the pyroxene by magnetite. Quartz and perthitic orthoclase are intersertal to the other minerals, and both contain euhedral apatite crystals. The apatite content of this rock is high (3 per cent); biotite also is relatively abundant.

A mile south of the line of section, the chilled upper rock of the layered series is exposed at the contact with the anorthositic gabbro in Miller Creek. Sample G580 (No. 8, Tables 4 and 5) from this contact rock is diabasic microsyenogabbro. Alteration of this rock by nearby red granophyre dikes has introduced quartz and potash feldspar, and destroyed any original olivine.

At Bardon Peak, at the base of the gabbro at the southern limit of exposure (Secs. 33 and 34, T.49N., R.15W.), the rock is a banded troctolite (No. 10, Tables 4 and 5). An alternation of olivine-rich and plagioclase-rich layers forms banding that may show gravitational stratification (Figs. 5 and 6). A chemical analysis of this rock, M4634, is given in Table 9, No. VII. The banded troctolite contains labradorite (An_{65}) in medium-sized tabular crystals oriented approximately parallel to the banding. Olivine (Fa_{39}) is in small rounded grains. Augite in narrow rims surrounding the olivine is intersertal, and probably formed only as interprecipitate material. Magnetite is in subhedral grains, probably of the primary precipitate phase. Alteration in the rock is minor, with small amounts of serpentine developed from olivine.

Troctolite and olivine gabbro are the most common rock types along the bluff overlooking the St. Louis River from Bardon Peak to Rest

FIGURE 5.—Rhythmic banding in troctolite on Skyline Drive at Bardon Peak. Alternation of olivine-rich and plagioclase-rich layers is accentuated by differential weathering.

FIGURE 6.—Gravity stratification resembling graded bedding in banded troctolite at Bardon Peak. Upward transition from feldspathic layers into olivine-rich layers is abrupt, but the transition from olivine-rich to feldspar-rich is gradational.
(Six-inch ruler in photo indicates scale.)

Point (on Highway 61, center Sec. 14, T.49N., R.15W.). At Rest Point the chief rock type is a banded olivine gabbro in which olivine-rich, feldspar-rich, and magnetite-ilmenite-rich bands are found. The mode of sample P55G (Table 4, No. 11) represents the average composition of five slides from the banded rock. The banding is parallel to fluxion structure. Olivine (Fa_{42}) is in small rounded grains. Augite and minor inverted pigeonite (Fs_{34}) are intersertal or ophitic. Figure 7 shows a large poikilitic augite crystal from this locality.

Outcrops northeast of Rest Point consist of three gabbroic types: (1) anorthositic gabbro inclusions, derived from the older period of activity; (2) banded olivine gabbro, which surrounds the anorthositic gabbro inclusions; and (3) nearly massive gabbro that intrudes the two older rock types. Contorted banding was produced by flow in the youngest gabbro around the inclusions. This zone of three intermixed gabbros extends to the contact of the layered series and the anorthositic gabbro at Keene Creek. The early banded rock at Keene Creek (M3771, No. 12, Tables 4 and 5) has plagioclase-rich layers alternating with mafic-rich

FIGURE 7.—Poikilitic augite enclosing rounded grains of olivine and small plagioclase crystals. The size difference between the plagioclase crystals enclosed in the augite and the crystals outside the augite indicates that the augite partly formed as a precipitate crystal, and by surrounding the plagioclase laths cut them off from additions by the interprecipitate liquid. Sample P55G. 7½X, crossed nicols.

layers that contain varying amounts of olivine, augite, ilmenite, and orthopyroxene (inverted pigeonite). The more massive gabbro (M3772, No. 13, Tables 4 and 5) intruding the banded rock is a hypersthene syenogabbro with quartz and orthoclase as intersertal minerals. The two gabbros at these localities are younger than the anorthositic gabbro and have been mapped with the layered series. In the field they could be distinguished only where cross-cutting relations were clear.

Peridotite was reported by Grout (1918b, p. 629) in the banded gabbro a few yards above the base at Bardon Peak, along the tracks of the Duluth, Winnipeg and Pacific Railroad. The peridotite is not a layer in the gabbro, but instead intrudes the banded troctolite (Fig. 8). A second, probably unrelated occurrence was noted just off Skyline Drive at Bardon Peak, where inclusions of peridotite as much as three feet across in troctolite are stained by the weathering of chalcopyrite. This rock is chiefly olivine with abundant magnetite-ilmenite and augite.

Mineral Trends in the Layered Series. The minerals in the layered series of the Duluth Gabbro Complex vary somewhat in composition,

FIGURE 8.—Apophysis of peridotite cutting banded troctolite. An offshoot of the peridotite in the Bardon Peak intrusion cuts across the banding of troctolite in the layered series; the locality is close to the upper railroad track on Bardon Peak.
(Six-inch ruler in photo indicates scale.)

24

but the variation is not a regular function of height in the mass (see Table 6). Immersion liquids and a four-axis Leitz universal stage were used in the study of these minerals. The Rittman zone method and the tables of Kennedy (1947, p. 562) were used to determine the anorthite content of the plagioclase.

PLAGIOCLASE

Three types of zoning are present in the plagioclase: (1) simple normal zoning from a uniform calcic core to a sodic outer rim; (2) oscillatory zoning with several zones of alternating composition; and (3) corrosion zoning. The simple normal zoning reflects the trend toward increased soda content as the interprecipitate material crystallized. This type of zoning is present in almost all the rocks, though it is much less prominent in rocks in which the precipitate crystals were closely packed by orientation of crystals.

The compositional range of the plagioclase crystals in the layered series is An_{53-67}; the average composition is about An_{60}. The crystals almost invariably have albite twinning; Carlsbad and pericline twins are abundant, and other types are rare. Wedged and bent twin lamellae in certain rocks resulted from mechanical deformation. Minute rods of opaque material, oriented in three directions controlled by the plagioclase lattice, cloud the central zones of many crystals.

OLIVINE

Olivine generally occurs in small rounded grains as part of the precipitate phase (Wager, 1953), and only rarely (Fig. 3) is poikilitic or intersertal. It ranges in composition from Fa_{39} to Fa_{47}; only two measured samples were above Fa_{44}. Leighton (1954) found a greater variation in the gabbro of northern Wisconsin, Fa_{27} to Fa_{52}. More magnesian olivine is known from the Duluth gabbro farther to the north. One sample from the Kawishiwi River (see Fig. 1) near the base of the gabbro complex is Fa_{28}. The rocks at Duluth which show iron-enrichment in the pyroxenes do not contain olivine, and contain quartz.

CLINOPYROXENE

The clinopyroxene in gabbros of the layered series is a light-purplish-brown titanaugite that has well-developed schiller structure. It has a rounded habit in a few of the melanocratic rocks, indicating crystallization in the precipitate phase. In most rocks the augite crystals are poikilitic or intersertal, surrounding or crystallizing between precipitate olivine and plagioclase. Nearly simultaneous crystallization of orthopyroxene (inverted pigeonite) and clinopyroxene is indicated by the textural relations.

TABLE 7. CHEMICAL ANALYSES AND OPTICAL PROPERTIES
OF TITANAUGITES
(after Hess, 1949, pp. 658–659)

	3	4	5
Chemical Analyses			
SiO_2	50.79	50.76	50.85
Al_2O_3	3.48	2.83	2.70
Fe_2O_3	1.37	1.35	1.11
FeO	9.41	10.23	10.36
MgO	14.64	14.22	14.09
CaO	18.55	19.08	19.20
Na_2O	.36	.32	.30
K_2O	.03	.00	.00
H_2O+	.03	.02	.01
H_2O-	.04	.01	.01
TiO_2	1.03	.99	1.05
Cr_2O_3	.25	.19	.13
MnO	.24	.25	.25
NiO	.03	.02	.02
	100.25	100.27	100.16
Optical Properties			
2V	43½	46¾	47
alpha	1.6930	1.6941	1.6937
beta	1.6968	1.6984	1.6982
gamma	1.7215	1.7218	1.7221
Z ∧ c	43½	44	44

3. Analysis 28, Specimen No. 9639, titanaugite from fine-grained biotite gabbro, 150 yards NE of top of inclined railway at small quarry, Duluth (from microgabbro dike cutting anorthositic gabbro). R. B. Ellestad, analyst.

4. Analysis 29, Specimen No. D3, titanaugite from coarse diabase pegmatite, bluff east of Dutchman's Lake, Sec. 7, T.63N., R.6E., Cook County, Minnesota. R. B. Ellestad, analyst.

5. Analysis 30, Specimen No. D2, titanaugite from pegmatitic zone in gabbro sill, shore of Lake Superior, Sec. 35, T.63N., R.5E., Cook County, Minnesota. R. B. Ellestad, analyst.

The optic angle and the *gamma* index were determined for a number of samples (Table 5), and the compositions were plotted on Figure 9. Only a small variation was found in the optical properties of the titanaugites from different parts of the gabbro. The compositional variation is not systematic with height in the intrusion except when combined with pyroxenes from ferrogranodiorite and granophyre.

Three analyses of titanaugites from northeastern Minnesota have been published by Hess (1949, p. 658–659). The color, optic angle, and indices of these pyroxenes (Table 7) are similar to those from the Duluth gabbro. This similarity emphasizes the uniformity of the clinopyroxenes from various sources, although none of the analyzed samples is from the gabbro proper. The one analyzed sample reported as being from the Duluth Gabbro Complex is actually from a microgabbro dike that

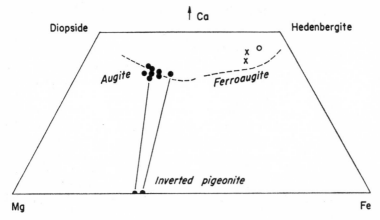

ATOMIC PERCENT

FIGURE 9.—Comparison of composition of pyroxenes from the Duluth Complex with the trend of crystallization from the Skaergaard Complex.

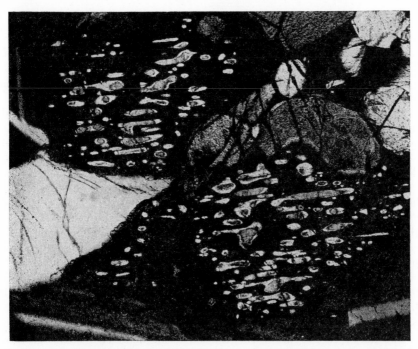

FIGURE 10.—Oriented blebs of clinopyroxene in hypersthene host, the result of inversion from pigeonite. Exsolved clinopyroxene, probably ferroaugite, in hypersthene host; the hypersthene is molded around crystals of labradorite and olivine. Sample G1019, Sec. 5, T.49N., R.15W. 115X, crossed nicols.

27

cuts the anorthositic gabbro. The other analyzed samples are from basic pegmatites.

ORTHOPYROXENE

Orthopyroxene formed by inversion from pigeonite is found in most of the rocks of the layered series. The habit of the orthopyroxene is similar to the clinopyroxene. Ophitic crystals are common, and the edges of the pyroxene are molded around earlier minerals. Exsolution lamellae in two directions indicate inversion from pigeonite. A coarse set of lamellae is augite or ferroaugite (Fig. 10) that developed before inversion from pigeonite. A second set of fine diopside lamellae parallels the optic plane and developed after inversion (Hess, 1941). The exsolution lamellae extend nearly to the edges of the crystals, indicating that even the late additions to the edges of the crystals from the interprecipitate liquid formed originally as pigeonite.

Small amounts of wormy or fibrous orthopyroxene form intergrowths with plagioclase, often rimming olivine. This intergrowth (Fig. 4) probably formed in the late magmatic or deuteric stage.

BARDON PEAK INTRUSION

A tabular intrusive body of gabbroic rocks that cuts the banded troctolite at Bardon Peak (Pl. 1) is designated the Bardon Peak Intrusion. The unit is approximately 200 feet thick, dips irregularly about 35°NE, and can be traced for about a mile and a half. It is banded and contains olivine gabbro, feldspathic gabbro, and peridotite.

The upper contact of the mass is well exposed on both the upper and lower railroad tracks on Bardon Peak. Low cuts on the upper tracks show peridotite with inclusions of the banded gabbro, and apophyses of peridotite transgressing the older banded troctolite (Fig. 8). The peridotite is coarse-grained even at the contact.

Coarse-grained olivine gabbro intrudes the banded troctolite of the layered series on the lower railroad tracks. The rock is coarse-grained even at the contact, suggesting that the banded troctolite was hot at the time of intrusion of the olivine gabbro. These contact relations indicate that the Bardon Peak Intrusion was emplaced in the second major period of basic igneous activity, shortly after the lower part of the layered series crystallized.

The lower contact of the Bardon Peak Intrusion is not well exposed, but its position is known fairly accurately at the southern end of exposures.

The major rock type of the Bardon Peak mass is a coarse-grained light-colored poikilitic olivine gabbro (Table 8, No. XI); it is well exposed at the upper contact of the unit on the tracks of the Northern Pacific Railroad at Bardon Peak. Poikilitic augite crystals as much as

TABLE 8. CHEMICAL ANALYSES OF GABBROIC ROCKS FROM THE DULUTH AREA

	VII	8	9	10	XI	12
SiO_2	47.36	48.20	49.39	42.24	46.90	32.90
Al_2O_3	18.81	19.53	29.08	18.50	15.68	1.59
Fe_2O_3	1.30	tr	.34	4.68	1.23	13.25
FeO	10.65	10.60	2.89	14.50	10.58	21.06
MgO	8.59	9.28	2.26	2.76	8.61	20.14
CaO	8.33	8.51	13.06	10.36	10.11	.50
Na_2O	2.94	2.52	2.89	2.19	2.32	tr
K_2O	.42	.32	.10	.33	.57	tr
H_2O+	.24	.65	.34	1.80	.86	4.56
H_2O-	.05	.08	.09	.25	.14	.55
CO_2	.01	.02	tr	1.67	.03	.10
TiO_2	1.10	.65	tr	1.16	2.59	5.36
P_2O_5	.11	.19	.09	.19	.10	tr
MnO	.14	.14	.04	.13	.16	.40
S		.03	.00			.05
SrO	.01					
Cr_2O_3			tr			.04
Cu_2O						.15
"Rarer elements"						.06
	100.06	100.72	100.57	100.76	99.80	100.71

VII. *Layered Series*: Banded troctolite. Bardon Peak, on upper tracks of Canadian National Railroad, Cat. No. M4634. Doris Thaemlitz, analyst.

8. *Layered Series*: Olivine gabbro, West Duluth, Sec. 23, T.49N., R.15W. F. F. Grout, analyst (Grout, 1918b, p. 646, No. 1).

9. *Anorthositic gabbro (?)*: Anorthosite, north of Proctor, Sec. 19, T.50N., R.14W. F. F. Grout, analyst (Grout, 1918b, p. 646, No. 3). Inclusion in layered series?

10. *Basic Pegmatite*: Gabbro pegmatite, Short Line Park, Sec. 33, T.49N., R.15W. G. S. Nishihara, analyst (Grout, 1918b, p. 646, No. 5).

XI. *Intrusion at Bardon Peak*: Olivine gabbro, Bardon Peak, lower tracks of Canadian National Railroad, Cat. No. M4633, Doris Thaemlitz, analyst.

12. *Intrusion at Bardon Peak*: Peridotite, Short Line Park, Sec. 34, T.49N., R.15W. F. F. Grout, analyst (Grout, 1918b, p. 646, No. 2).

five inches across contain tabular plagioclase (An_{65}) and small rounded olivine (Fa_{40}) grains. Magnetite-ilmenite and apatite are accessory minerals, and a trace of serpentine formed from the olivine. A small amount of medium-grained olivine gabbro near troctolite in composition was found in outcrops to the north in Section 28, T.49N., R.15W.

Peridotite is the major rock type exposed on the Duluth, Winnipeg and Pacific Railroad tracks near the top of the Bardon Peak mass. The layer is somewhat more than 50 feet thick; other mafic layers alternate with feldspar-rich layers in the cuts to the west. None of the peridotite is fresh; serpentine, chlorite, and talc make up almost half of the rock. Primary plagioclase (An_{68}) has been partly replaced by light-green serpentine, as shown by relict albite twinning. Olivine (Fa_{42}) is the most common primary mineral, and magnetite-ilmenite and augite are present in considerable amounts. A chemical analysis of this rock is given in Table 8, No. 12.

BASIC PEGMATITES

Gabbro pegmatite intrudes rocks of the layered series and the re-crystallized basalt flows beneath the gabbro at several localities. Peg-matites of similar composition formed by segregation in the anorthositic gabbro have been discussed earlier.

Most of the gabbro pegmatites in the Duluth area intrude the banded troctolite and the basalt flows near Bardon Peak. The pegmatites are tabular, have no consistent orientation, and generally cut across the structure of the host rock. The observed maximum thickness of indi-vidual bodies is about eight feet, and lengths of 40 feet can be seen in the high cuts along the railroads. Many dikes are zoned from a coarse-grained olivine gabbro pegmatite at the margins to a fine-grained gran-ophyre or granite in a discontinuous zone in the center. The marginal pegmatite has large titanaugite crystals up to six inches in length rudely oriented perpendicular to the walls. Labradorite (An_{60}) and olivine (Fa_{46}) are present in considerable amounts, and apatite, magnetite-ilmenite, and biotite are common accessory minerals. An intermediate zone of altered feldspar, uralite, biotite, quartz, and potash feldspar grades to the central zone of alkali feldspar and quartz.

Not all of the granophyre in the pegmatites can be attributed to dif-ferentiation of the parent gabbro within the dike. The volume of grano-phyre is too great in some dikes, and the granophyre is asymmetrically located in others. One thick dike has a screen of basalt hornfels that separates the granophyre on one side from the basic pegmatite. Gran-ophyre dikes and irregular masses cut the basalt flows and banded troc-tolite in this area, and these independent intrusive bodies probably fol-lowed zones of weakness in some of the pegmatites, though the small amounts of granophyre in others may have been formed by differentia-tion.

About a mile southeast of the Duluth Municipal Airport (SE¼ Sec. 7, T.50N., R.15W.) a gabbro pegmatite dike intrudes banded olivine gabbro; the contacts are sharp. Augite crystals are oriented rudely per-pendicular to the wall in the outer part of the pegmatite and grade through altered material to irregular cores of pink aplite.

Grout (1918f) previously suggested that the magma that formed the basic pegmatites separated as an immiscible liquid before the gabbroic rocks were formed. His hypothesis was based on observations that dis-tinct dikes were present only in the flows outside the gabbro, and that all the pegmatites were near the base of the mass. These points were not borne out by the recent field work; the dike near the airport has sharp contacts and is located in the upper third of the layered series.

The basic pegmatites seem to represent slightly differentiated liquids, perhaps derived from the interprecipitate liquid in a series of layered crystal accumulates. The liquids, perhaps richer in volatiles than the parent magma, moved into fractures after consolidation of the main mass of rock. They crystallized from the walls inward, but slowly enough for giant crystals of pyroxene and plagioclase to be formed. A part of the last material to form differentiated to yield granophyre. Some quantity of the liquids probably moved considerable distances; accordingly, it is probable that the large amount of granophyre seen in a few of the dikes does not represent differentiation from the visible basic rock.

FERROGRANODIORITE, ADAMELLITE, AND SYENODIORITE

Medium-grained, dark-colored, pyroxene ferrogranodiorite, adamellite, and syenodiorite are present in three major bodies, and form several small dikes. The most abundant type is ferrogranodiorite which in composition of the plagioclase and pyroxene and in iron content resembles the ferrogabbros of the Skaergaard Intrusion (Wager and Deer, 1939).

The largest mass of ferrogranodiorite crops out along Miller and Coffee creeks in Secs. 29 and 20, T.50N., R.14W. Exposures along the eastern side show a fine-grained border phase of syenodiorite (M4666, Table 9). Apophyses of syenodiorite extend from the main mass into the anortho-

TABLE 9. MODES (VOLUME PER CENT) OF FERROGRANODIORITE, ADAMELLITE, SYENODIORITE, AND GRANOPHYRE

	1	2	3	4	5	6	7	8
Plagioclase	44	36	47	72	50	55	30	31
Orthoclase	11	14	4	5	8	11	41	25
Quartz	7	9	2	,	p	7	9	14
Pyroxene	19	7	31	10	11	18	11	19
Hornblende	12	17	11	p	10	p		
Magnetite	4	5	8	8	8	9	9	10
Apatite	2	2	1	p	1	p	p	p
Biotite	1	p			10			
Sphene				p		p	p	
Pyrite	p		p					
Epidote				p		p		p
Chlorite	p	10	p	p	p	p	p	p
Uralite	p	p	p	p	p	p	p	p
Johannsen No.	(227)	(227″)	(2211′)	(227)	(2211′)	(227)	(226″)	(227″)

1. Ferrogranodiorite, M3781. Quarry in Coffee Creek, Sec. 20, T.50N., R.14W.
2. Adamellite, M3738. Near Miller Creek, Sec. 29, T.50N., R.14W.
3. Syenodiorite, M4666. Chilled phase above quarry in Coffee Creek, Sec. 20, T.50N., R.14W.
4. Ferrogranodiorite, M4625. Sec. 30, T.50N., R.14W.
5. Syenodiorite, M4618. Dike in Sec. 30, T.50N., R.14W.
6. Ferrogranodiorite, M4625-7. Skyline Drive, near Enger Tower, Sec. 28, T.50N., R.14W.
7. Granophyre, P57G. Enger Tower intrusion, quarry at 12th Avenue W., Sec. 28, T.50N., R.14W.
8. Granophyre, M3708-7. Enger Tower intrusion, Sec. 28, T.50N., R.14W. (Mode from Lucia, 1954.)

sitic gabbro, and blocks of the anorthositic gabbro are found in the syenodiorite and granodiorite. Blocks of fine-grained basic rock are included
within the ferrogranodiorite and probably were derived from the chill
zone of the layered series. The inclusions show the initial stages of a
granoblastic texture, with sugary grain, globular pyroxene, and sutured
plagioclase. Some inclusions are cut by red stringers of quartz and perthitic feldspar derived from the granodiorite magma. The ferrogranodiorite
was intruded along the contact zone between the layered series and the
anorthositic gabbro. It represents either a separate intrusion or late
movement of differentiated magma from the layered series. The poor
exposures to the north do not permit tracing the intrusion beyond the
quarry in Coffee Creek, but the ferrogranodiorite may continue for some
distance.

The quarry in Sec. 20, T.50N., R.14W. is in massive ferrogranodiorite (M3781, Table 9) with a few pegmatitic concentrations of quartz
and feldspar. The ferrogranodiorite is a medium-grained rock with pink
feldspars set in a dark matrix. The plagioclase is zoned, with relatively
uniform cores of about An_{44}, but with rims that grade sharply to albite.

TABLE 10. CHEMICAL ANALYSES OF FERROGRANODIORITES

	XIII	XIV	XV
SiO_2	50.13	53.78	50.36
Al_2O_3	11.72	16.34	14.88
Fe_2O_3	2.30	4.66	7.19
FeO	11.99	7.65	8.14
MgO	3.32	1.31	2.36
CaO	6.74	7.08	7.06
Na_2O	2.90	4.07	3.74
K_2O	2.16	1.76	1.68
H_2O+	1.09	.65	.87
H_2O-	.36	.32	.21
CO_2	.04	.03	.01
TiO_2	2.93	1.55	2.15
P_2O_5	1.53	.54	.83
MnO	.24	.18	.20
BaO	.02		
SrO	.03	.04	.03
S	.07		
Rb_2O	.01	.00	.00
	99.58	99.96	99.71
Less $O \cong S$	—.03		
	99.55		

XIII. Ferrogranodiorite, M3781. Quarry in Coffee Creek, Sec.
20, T.50N., R.14W. Doris Thaemlitz, analyst.

XIV. Ferrogranodiorite, M4624. Intrusion in NW¼ Sec. 28,
T.50N., R.14W. R. B. Taylor, analyst.

XV. Ferrogranodiorite intrusion, M4625. Outcrop on Skyline
Drive south of Twin Lakes and northeast of Enger Tower.
R. B. Taylor, analyst.

Brown pleochroic hornblende in fresh crystals, ferroaugite, and magnetite are the most abundant primary mafic minerals. Most of the ferroaugite is altered to uralite and chlorite and to an associated light-brown mineral that may be stilpnomelane. Orthoclase, albite, and quartz are late intersertal minerals in which apatite is concentrated. The extensive alteration forming uralite and chlorite suggests high-temperature volatile activity. A chemical analysis of this rock is included in Table 10, No. XIII.

A sample from Miller Creek, from the same ferrogranodiorite body, is similar in mineralogy, but is less altered. The pyroxene in this rock is a ferroaugite with $2V = 57°$ and $beta = 1.725$. Andesine, An_{42}, has fairly uniform cores, but grades to albite at the edges. The hornblende crystallized later than the ferroaugite, and replaced it in part. Skeletal magnetite and euhedral apatite are accessory minerals. Potash feldspar and the late albite form perthite and antiperthite, and both have a hematite dusting giving them a pink color. The potash feldspar and quartz are late and are molded around other minerals, and in a few places seem to replace the edges of some of the andesine crystals. Minor amounts of zircon occur as two types of crystals, one blocky and altered, the other long, euhedral, and clear.

The border rock is a fine- to medium-grained dark syenodiorite (M4666, Table 9) that is similar to the granodiorite but contains less quartz and potash feldspar. The texture also is similar; pyroxene, plagioclase, and hornblende show relations of simultaneous crystallization, and later quartz and potash feldspar occur between the grains.

Half a mile east of the ferrogranodiorite of Miller Creek, in NW¼ Sec. 28, T.50N., R.14W., a tabular intrusion of ferrogranodiorite cuts the anorthositic gabbro. The upper contact is complex, with apophyses of ferrogranodiorite extending into the anorthosite gabbro. The mass strikes about N.70°W., dips about 40°N., has a maximum thickness of about 100 feet, and is exposed for about a third of a mile. Samples from this intrusion are similar to the rock at Miller Creek. The analyzed sample (Table 10, No. XIV) represents rock from near the middle of the mass.

Several small ferrogranodiorite dikes cut the anorthositic gabbro in Sec. 30, T.50N., R.14W. A common trend (N.10°E.) and similar lithology indicate a single period of intrusion, probably related to that of the granodiorite masses of Section 28 and of Miller Creek. A seven-foot-wide syenodiorite dike that can be traced about 50 feet (M4618, Table 9, No. 5) closely resembles border phases of the Miller Creek mass.

FERROGRANODIORITE-GRANOPHYRE ASSOCIATION

A steeply dipping irregular intrusive body of granodiorite and granophyre crops out just east of Enger Tower (Goldich, Taylor, and Lucia,

FIGURE 11.—Flow banding in ferrogranodiorite. Outcrop on Skyline Drive northeast of
Enger Tower and south of Twin Lakes in composite intrusion
of ferrogranodiorite and granophyre.

1956). Flow banding in the granodiorite indicates that this body strikes about N.27°E. and dips 57°SE. Inclusions of anorthositic gabbro and apophyses of granophyre are numerous and destroy any regularity of form.

Two main zones are distinguished in the intrusion, but the relations between them are not clear. The lower part, cropping out on the western side, is ferrogranodiorite that has a high mafic content, giving it a dark- to medium-gray color. The upper part is granophyre having a small mafic mineral-content and a brick-red color. The zone between the two types is poorly exposed, and two interpretations are possible. The two rocks could represent separate intrusions with reaction at the contact producing a gradation; more probably, however, the two rocks represent a change in composition of the magma from granodiorite to granophyre during the time that the magma was being intruded. Movements of the granodiorite magma produced strong flow banding (Fig. 11).

The anorthositic gabbro is altered adjacent to the granophyre, and quartz and alkali feldspar have been introduced. Grout and Longley (1935) have described the rock from the quarry at 13th Avenue and 3rd Street as contaminated "red rock." Some of the anorthositic gabbro inclusions have corroded edges, and a few are ghost-like remnants due to almost complete reaction with the granophyre magma. Sharp contacts with other blocks indicate a shorter period of reaction. Differential weathering emphasizes the alteration in the gabbro; the sericitized edges of the plagioclase remain in relief, whereas the central part of the feldspar and the uralitized augite form low areas.

The ferrogranodiorite from the basal zone (M4625, Mode, Table 9, No. 4; Analysis XV, Table 10) is a medium-grained dark-gray rock. The plagioclase is zoned, with cores about An_{53} and an average composition near An_{47}. The plagioclase is partly sericitized, and the edges are corroded by late-crystallizing perthitic orthoclase. The clinopyroxene is ferroaugite, $2V = 54°$; it is intensely altered to uralite. Magnetite, apatite, sphene, and pyrite are accessory minerals. The proportions of light and dark minerals are variable in the banded zone, which has both planar and linear structures; most of the rock, however, is massive.

The granophyre of this intrusion is massive, and has andesine cores surrounded and armored by potash feldspar that grades to a granophyric matrix. The cores are about An_{34}; they have narrow albite twin lamellae. There is a small amount of ferroaugite, but the relative abundance of uralite indicates that much more crystallized originally. The ferroaugite has a $2V = 60°$ and a *beta* index of about 1.729. Magnetite, apatite, and zircon are accessory minerals. Two modes are given in Table 9 (M3708-7 and P57G). These represent specimens from the Enger Tower Intrusion.

GRANOPHYRE

Red granophyre that is younger than all the igneous rocks except the late basalt and microgabbro cuts the rocks of the Duluth Gabbro Complex. Small dikes can be found at almost all stratigraphic levels in the layered series, and are widely distributed in the anorthositic gabbro and in the overlying flows. The rock is variable in texture, but characteristically has a granophyric groundmass consisting of minutely intergrown quartz and red-dusted potassium feldspar. A basalt dike is chilled against the granophyre mass along Skyline Drive just northeast of Enger Tower, and an apophysis of the Endion sill (Pl. 1) cuts granophyre at Amity Creek.

Textural varieties of granophyre that are similar to the varieties found at Duluth have been illustrated previously by Leighton (1954, p. 418). The cuneiform type has a regular pattern of wedge-shaped intergrowths of quartz and feldspar. The myrmekitic type has curved worm-like patches of quartz. The radiating-fringe type has a central core of feldspar from which the quartz-feldspar intergrowth radiates outward. The irregular granophyre type has a poorly developed intergrowth and approaches a granitoid texture, but quartz and feldspar interpenetrate coarsely. At Duluth, the varieties are gradational, and several types may occur in an individual intrusion.

The alkali feldspar is an intergrowth of potassium feldspar (orthoclase) and albite in varying proportions, and accordingly perthite and antiperthite occur in the same rock. The feldspar is clouded by a heavy dusting of hematite and kaolinite that partly obscures the perthitic intergrowth. The quartz is intimately intergrown with feldspar, and may be difficult to recognize in hand specimen. Local pegmatitic spots, miarolitic cavities, and changes in proportion of ferromagnesian minerals give the rock a varied appearance.

An abandoned quarry on Kenwood Avenue (Sec. 15, T.50N., R.14W.) exposes granophyre that intrudes basalt flows (Pl. 1). The granophyre is a sodic granite, partly altered, that has a coarse irregular implication texture. Albite, near An_{01}, has well-developed chessboard twinning, a combination of albite and pericline twins in which no individual extends entirely across a grain. Perthitic orthoclase and quartz seem to corrode the albite. Chlorite may have been derived from the alteration of original amphibole or pyroxene. Even the freshest samples contain about 5 per cent epidote, and suggest (Harpum, 1954) contamination by the basalt flows. Magnetite-ilmenite intergrowths with typical triangular pattern (exsolution of ilmenite along the octahedral planes of magnetite) have been altered to magnetite-leucoxene intergrowths. Dikes of the fresh-appearing red granophyre extend into the basalt flows as apophyses from the larger mass, and have sharp contacts and rotated inclusions with sharp contacts. These features indicate a magmatic origin.

Near the center of the body, the granophyre contains inclusions of altered basalt that can be distinguished only by a ghost-like outline and by their darker color. The inclusions show all stages of replacement, from almost complete reconstitution to almost no alteration. Some inclusions show a peculiar local alteration that has resulted from the formation of an amphibole—probably a calcic hornblende—ringed with red-dusted alkali feldspar in what probably were amygdales. Such alteration in inclusions from near the border of the granophyre is shown in Figure 12. The inclusions near the contact derived from the bordering basalt are the least altered; those near the center of the granophyre mass are the most thoroughly replaced, probably as a consequence of being in contact with the granophyric liquid for a considerable time.

Granophyre exposed along Amity Creek (Sec. 1, T.50N., R.14W.) has a somewhat variable texture. The coarser varieties have an irregular

FIGURE 12.—Basalt flow inclusions in red granophyre in quarry on Kenwood Avenue. Potassium feldspar and quartz have been introduced into the basalt, and are concentrated in spots that were probably amygdules. The rotated blocks indicate intrusion of the granophyre as a magma, though it probably replaced some of the basalt.

implication texture (Fig. 13), and the finer varieties have minutely inter-grown fan-like structures radiating out from central points (Fig 14). This granophyre intrudes the anorthositic gabbro, and is intruded by an apophysis of the Endion sill (Pl. 1). Similar granophyre along Jean Duluth Road (Sec. 1, T.50N., R.14W.) is separated by the Endion sill from the Amity Creek outcrops, but probably was originally a part of the same intrusion. Most of this granophyre resembles the coarser phase of the Amity Creek granophyre.

Granophyre on Woodland Avenue (Sec. 2, T.50N., R.14W.) is lo-cated near the top of the anorthositic gabbro, but contacts are not ex-posed. The rock is similar to the fine-grained granophyre on Amity Creek, and has minutely intergrown radiating structures of quartz and alkali feldspar.

Numerous small dikes and irregular bodies of red granophyre are sim-ilar to the larger masses previously described. Most are leucocratic rocks with quartz and feldspar in coarse irregular intergrowths. Amphi-bole, ferroaugite, and magnetite have been partly altered to chlorite, uralite, and hematite. Calcite was formed in a late deuteric or hydro-thermal stage. A heavy red hematite dusting generally obscures the

FIGURE 13.—Granophyre. Altered albite crystals have heavily dusted red rims that grade into the granophyric intergrowth of the matrix. Sample M4657. 35X.

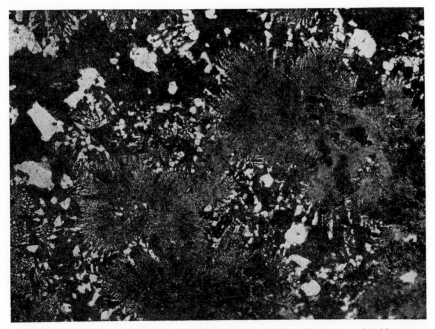

FIGURE 14.—Spherulitic granophyre. Radiating intergrowths of quartz and feldspar are surrounded by coarser, more irregular intergrowths of the same minerals. Sample M4652. 35X.

feldspars. Chemical and modal analyses for a number of the granophyre dikes are given in Tables 11, 12, and 13.

An uncommon high-silica granophyre exposed along Skyline Drive in Sec. 32, T.50N., R.14W. occurs along the contact between the anorthositic gabbro and the chilled phase of the layered series. Sample M3764 (Analysis XIX, Table 11; Mode 6, Table 12) is an albite granophyre with irregular granophyric texture. The granophyre penetrates the chilled basalt of the layered series in narrow irregular zones, apparently localized by fractures. Alteration of the basalt and replacement by the granophyre-forming fluid has rounded the corners of the blocks, introduced quartz and alkali feldspar, and formed uralite from pyroxene. The alteration of the anorthositic gabbro is limited to the immediate contact and to widely spaced fractures. The unusual composition of this granophyre is difficult to explain if it formed from a magma, and an origin by replacement seems probable.

Granophyre dikes exposed only a few blocks from the occurrence along Skyline Drive had highly variable effects on the country rock. Granophyre intruding the chill zone of the layered series on Miller Creek contains fresh fragments of basalt and the granophyre dikes have sharp con-

TABLE 11. PARTIAL CHEMICAL ANALYSES OF GRANOPHYRES

	16	XVII	XVIII	XIX	XX	XXI	XXII	XXIII	XXIV	XXV
Fe_2O_3X*	4.36	2.83	2.37	.39	2.67	2.53	7.17	3.59	.87	5.01
FeO*	3.93	3.54	1.09	.47	3.51	2.80	1.80	3.68	2.25	.22
Na_2O†	3.45	4.03	2.85	6.24	4.62	3.84	3.24	3.69	2.76	1.93
K_2O†	3.98	4.44	5.40	.40	3.04	4.34	5.03	4.04	5.70	6.28
Rb_2O§					.01	.02	.02	.02		

* Determinations on Samples XX–XXV by S. S. Goldich.
† Determinations on Samples XX–XXIII by R. B. Taylor; XXIV and XXV by James Markham.
§ Rb_2O by flame spectrophotometer, E. L. Horstman, analyst.
16. Granophyre, NW corner, Sec. 27, T.50N., R.14W. F. F. Grout, analyst (Grout, 1918, p. 650, No. 25). Complete analysis, Table 13, No. 16.
XVII. Granophyre, M4628. Bardon Peak, Sec. 27, T.49N., R.15W. R. B. Taylor, analyst. Complete analysis, Table 13, No. XVII.
XVIII. Granophyric aplitic granite, M3787. R. B. Taylor, analyst. Complete analysis, Table 13, No. XVIII.
XIX. Granophyre, M3764. Skyline Drive above ore docks. Doris Thaemlitz, analyst. Complete analysis, Table 13, No. XIX.
XX. Granophyre, M4654. Kenwood Avenue quarry, Sec. 15, T.50N., R.14W.
XXI. Granophyre, M4656. Woodland Avenue, Sec. 2, T.50N., R.14W.
XXII. Granophyre, M4652. Near Forest Hill Cemetery, Sec. 35, T.51N., R.14W.
XXIII. Granophyre, M4657. Jean Duluth Road, Sec. 36, T.51N., R.14W.
XXIV. Granophyre. Near Finland, Minnesota, Sec. 17, T.57N., R.7W.
XXV. Granophyre. Dike cutting diabase, Silver Bay, Minnesota, Sec. 32, T.56N., R.7W.

TABLE 12. MODES (VOLUME PER CENT) OF GRANOPHYRES

	1	2	3	4	5	6	7	8
Feldspar	68	71	66	68	64	71	63	75
Quartz	18	20	25	17	29	24	36	17
Magnetite	4	5	2	3	1	p	p	1
Apatite	p		p	p	p	p	p	p
Sphene		p		p		1	p	
Zircon	p	p	p		p			p
Uralite	p	p	3	p	p	p		1
Epidote	p	p	p	5	p			p
Chlorite	7	5	4	7	4	2	p	p
Calcite	2	p	p	p	p	2	1	p
Leucoxene		p		p	p			p
Biotite								6
Johannsen No.	(216)	(216)	(216)	(217)	(215)	(218)	(218)	(216″)

1. Granophyre, M4657. Jean Duluth Road, Sec. 36, T.51N., R.14W.
2. Granophyre, M4652. Near Forest Hill Cemetery, Sec. 35, T.51N., R.14W.
3. Granophyre, M4656. On Woodland Avenue, Sec. 2, T.50N., R.14W.
4. Granophyre, M4654. Kenwood Avenue quarry, Sec. 15, T.50N., R.14W.
5. Granophyric aplitic granite, M3787. Dike into dellenite flow, 8th Street, at 3rd Avenue W., Sec. 27, T.50N., R.14W.
6. Granophyre, M4638-d. Dike into layered series northeast of Rest Point, Sec. 12, T.49N., R.15W.
7. Granophyre, M3764. Skyline Drive at contact of anorthositic gabbro with layered series, Sec. 32, T.50N., R.14W.
8. Granophyre, M4628. Irregular intrusion cutting olivine gabbro at Bardon Peak, Sec. 33, T.49N., R.15W.

FIGURE 15.—Composite dike at 27th Avenue West and 12th Street. Anorthositic gabbro was first intruded by basalt, believed to be the chilled phase of the layered series, and then granophyre invaded the same zone of weakness. Ghost structures, the remains of replaced basalt, darken the red granophyre.

41

TABLE 13. CHEMICAL ANALYSES OF GRANOPHYRES

	16	XVII	XVIII	XIX
SiO₂	66.92	64.28	73.55	77.75
Al₂O₃	12.51	14.44	12.05	12.71
Fe₂O₃	4.36	2.83	2.37	.39
FeO	3.39	3.54	1.09	.47
MgO	1.66	1.76	.51	.34
CaO	1.20	1.03	.76	.68
Na₂O	3.45	4.03	2.85	6.24
K₂O	3.98	4.44	5.40	.40
H₂O+	1.25	1.21	.38	.38
H₂O−	.20	.95	.09	.13
CO₂	.02	.02	.16	.40
TiO₂	.69	.71	.27	.21
P₂O₅	.11	.15	.05	.01
MnO	.16	.07	.05	.01
BaO	.06	.09	.07	
SrO		.02	.01	
S	.04	.01	.01	
ZrO₂	.22			
	100.76	99.58	99.67	100.12
Less O ≅ S	−.01			
	100.75			

16. Granophyre ("red rock"), NW corner, Sec. 27, T.50N., R.14W. F. F. Grout, analyst (Grout, 1918b, p. 650, No. 25).

XVII. Granophyre, M4628. Bardon Peak, Sec. 27, T.49N., R.15W., irregular mass intruding olivine gabbro. R. B. Taylor, analyst.

XVIII. Granophyric aplitic granite, M3787. Dike intruding dellenite flow, 8th Street, at 3rd Avenue W., Duluth. R. B. Taylor, analyst.

XIX. Granophyre, M3764. Skyline Drive above ore docks, Sec. 32, T.50N., R.14W. Doris Thaemlitz, analyst.

tacts. In contrast, the effects of corrosion and replacement are well shown in the exposure at 27th Avenue West and 12th Street (Fig. 15). An intrusion of basaltic magma from the layered series chilled as a dike in the anorthositic gabbro. A later intrusion of granophyre followed the same zone of weakness, and blocks of basalt were rounded by corrosion leaving ghost-like remnants. Through-going movement is indicated, as the mafic content of the granophyre is too low to account for the material derived from the basalt.

LATE BASALT AND MICROGABBRO DIKE ROCKS

Basalt and microgabbro dikes are chilled against anorthositic gabbro, layered series gabbro, and granophyre host rocks. They represent the last major period of intrusion in the Duluth area. The largest dike of microgabbro with chilled basalt edges was intruded into the anorthositic gabbro north of Enger Tower (Pl. 1). The dike is about 80 feet thick, can be traced on the surface for about three quarters of a mile, and is probably the sill reported by Schwartz (1949, p. 56) in the Duluth sewer tunnel at 2nd Avenue West. The major part of this intrusion is ophitic microgabbro that contains labradorite (An_{64}), titanaugite, magnetite, and small amounts of uralite, with interstitial quartz and orthoclase. A chemical analysis of the clinopyroxene from this dike has been published by Hess (1949, p. 658), though reported as from "biotite gabbro." Analyses of basalt from the chill zone (Table 14, No. XXVI) and of microgabbro eight feet from the upper contact (Table 14, No. XXVII) are from rock exposed near the western end of the dike.

A swarm of dikes in the NE¼NW¼ Sec. 28, T.50N., R.14W. is probably related to the period of intrusion of the large microgabbro dike. These small dikes, from two inches to four feet in width, are nearly vertical, and trend N.65°E. The largest, just north of Twin Lakes along Skyline Drive, cuts the granophyre east of Enger Tower.

A microgabbro dike cuts the anorthositic gabbro in Sec. 36, T.50N., R.14W.; it strikes about N.80°E., and dips 50–80°S. It attains a maximum thickness of about 100 feet, but is only about 50 feet thick where

TABLE 14. CHEMICAL ANALYSES OF BASALT AND MICROGABBRO
DIKE ROCKS, AND LAYERED SERIES CHILL PHASE

	XXVI	XXVII	XXVIII	XXIX
SiO_2	49.18	49.21	49.65	
Al_2O_3	13.82	14.24	13.22	
Fe_2O_3	2.46	2.36	1.58	2.46
FeO	10.99	10.59	11.76	10.45
MgO	5.44	5.73	5.44	
CaO	9.16	9.14	8.98	
Na_2O	2.72	2.72	2.71	2.77
K_2O	.98	.97	.97	1.42
H_2O+	1.04	1.00	.59	
H_2O-	.20	.19	.18	
CO_2	.04	.02	.04	.56
TiO_2	2.99	2.83	3.93	
P_2O_5	.56	.50	.53	.31
MnO	.20	.19	.21	.20
S	.09	.07	.08	
	99.87	99.76	99.87	
Less $O \cong S$	−.03	−.03	−.03	
	99.84	99.73	99.84	

XXVI. Basalt, M3744-1. Chill zone of microgabbro dike near WFTV tower, Sec. 28, T.50N., R.14W. Eileen Oslund, analyst.

XXVII. Microgabbro, M3744-2. From same dike as above about eight feet from the contact, Sec. 28, T.50N., R.14W. Eileen Oslund, analyst.

XXVIII. Basalt, M3762. Dike intruding olivine gabbro and anorthositic gabbro, just off Haines Road, Sec. 36, T.50N., R.14W. Eileen Oslund, analyst.

XXIX. Basalt, P136G. Chill zone of layered series, Skyline Drive, above ore docks, Sec. 32, T.50N., R.14W. Doris Thaemlitz, analyst.

it is exposed along Skyline Parkway. The dike is exposed for about a mile as shown in Plate 1. This microgabbro dike is similar to the dike of comparable thickness exposed north of Enger Tower.

A small dike of fine-grained dense basalt that cuts the anorthositic gabbro was analyzed chemically (Table 14, No. XXVIII). The dike also cuts an olivine gabbro dike that is probably gabbro of the layered series. These relations are exposed in an outcrop just off Haines Road above the railroad tracks.

A microgabbro dike cuts the olivine gabbro of the layered series and shows chilled contacts. The exposures are in the northeast corner of Sec. 29, T.49N., R.14W. (Pl. 1). This dike probably was intruded during the same period as the others; it is younger than the second period of gabbro intrusion.

A microgabbro dike and several small basalt dikes cut the olivine gabbro of the layered series in the northeast corner of Sec. 28, T.50N., R.15W. The basalt is slightly porphyritic and contains plagioclase and olivine phenocrysts in a very fine-grained groundmass of plagioclase, pyroxene, and magnetite.

4. PETROLOGY

THE PROBLEM

Grout (1918b) considered the intrusive rocks at Duluth to be closely related and formed by processes of magmatic differentiation. He pointed out that a feldspathic gabbro, the anorthositic gabbro of this report, "was intruded and cooled before the main mass of more basic gabbro was intruded" (Grout, 1918b, p. 627). He attributed the accumulation of feldspar to the rising of lighter plagioclase crystals in the magma. Grout recognized that the banded gabbro at Duluth could not be explained simply by crystal settling, and appealed to convection operating together with crystal settling to produce bands or layers with the same minerals, but in proportions of startling contrast so that adjacent layers approach anorthosite on the one hand, and peridotite on the other. To explain the origin of the "red rock," Grout suggested immiscibility.

The present investigation, like that of Grout's, is largely restricted to the vicinity of Duluth. My more detailed studies have supplied data which answer some of the questions raised in Grout's work, yet at the same time raise many new problems.

SUMMARY OF HISTORY OF IGNEOUS ACTIVITY

The oldest recognized igneous activity in the Duluth region is represented by the Keweenawan flows that rest on the Puckwunge Formation or on the folded and eroded beds of the Thomson Formation. Small amounts of locally derived clastic material were deposited between outpourings of lava. The Keweenawan flows were intruded by the anorthositic gabbro, which probably was a crystal mush. Early phases of the anorthositic gabbro were broken up, and tectonic breccias were formed consisting of huge cognate inclusions. Rounded inclusions of anorthosite either could have been derived from an early phase of the anorthositic gabbro or from an older sequence at depth. Near the top of the anorthositic gabbro numerous inclusions of basalt derived from the Keweenawan lavas and the flows that formed the roof of the magma chamber near the contact were recrystallized to hornfels by the anorthositic gabbro.

The great bulk of the gabbroic rocks (the layered series) is attributed to fractional crystallization of basaltic magma. The rocks of the layered series, which include troctolite, olivine gabbro, gabbro, syenogabbro, and melanocratic phases of these types, are typically banded or layered, but a chilled phase of basalt or diabase was developed where the magma came in contact with the older, cold anorthositic gabbro. Rhythmic layering, gravity stratification, and fluxion structures show that the layered series rocks are essentially bottom crystal accumulates that precipitated in an environment of active circulation or convection of the magma; the differentiation trends produced by crystal settling, however, were modified by renewed intrusions of basaltic magma. It is impossible from currently available data to say how many times the magma was renewed during the development of the layered series.

Transgressive younger rocks of the Duluth Gabbro Complex range in composition from ferrogranodiorite to granite. These rocks cut both the anorthositic gabbro and the rocks of the layered series. At one locality, along Miller Creek, the ferrogranodiorite seems to grade through syenogabbro to gabbro of the layered series. Similarly, east of Enger Tower, the granodiorite seems to grade to granophyre; however, at both localities the sparsity of outcrops precludes positive conclusions.

Later dikes, mainly basalt or diabase, but including some of silicic composition, cut the granophyre and the older rock units. The Endion sill intrudes granophyre along Amity Creek; in turn it is cut by younger dikes of basalt that are chilled at the contacts, indicating that the sill had cooled before the dikes were emplaced.

THE LAYERED SERIES

Rhythmic layering and gravity stratification in some of the rocks at Duluth indicate positively that these rocks are bottom crystal-accumulates formed under conditions of magma movement. The cyclic banding suggests that convection currents were the cause of the movements. Probably the currents were local, for the larger layers are lenticular. The lack of a cryptic layering can best be explained by assuming that the composition of the magma was modified by renewed injection—earlier crystal phases were broken up and the regularity of mineralogic composition trends resulting from differentiation was destroyed.

In the upper part of the mass, along a line of section extending west from Enger Tower, there is a regular change in mineralogy; a rock and mineral series is formed that shows progressive enrichment in iron, silica, and alkalies:

gabbro ... syenogabbro ... ferrogranodiorite ...?... granophyre
An_{65-60} An_{55} An_{45} An_{35} An_1
    titanaugite   ferroaugite

The iron-enrichment in this series reaches a maximum at the ferrogranodiorite stage (Fig. 15), then decreases in the granophyre stage. The granophyres represent the culmination of enrichment in silica and alkalies (Fig. 15). Tectonic movements acted during crystallization to separate differentiated liquids and to produce some of the transgressive bodies that intrude the overlying anorthositic gabbro.

TRANSGRESSIVE FERROGRANODIORITE AND GRANOPHYRE

The ferrogranodiorite that intruded the anorthositic gabbro may have been derived from the magma of the layered series. The ferrogranodiorite body along Miller Creek could have crystallized from a magma that was differentiated essentially in place or that had moved a very short distance. The smaller bodies of ferrogranodiorite are clearly transgressive, indicating that the magma from which they crystallized was forced away from the site of differentiation. The ferrogranodiorite magma apparently was rich in volatiles because deuteric alteration is pervasive in all bodies.

All the granophyre masses are transgressive. Their origin probably is similar to that of the ferrogranodiorites. They represent a later differentiate, however, and may have formed from late liquids squeezed off by tectonic movements; subsequently, these liquids were intruded not only into the anorthositic gabbro but also into rocks of the layered series. Although some of the granophyre shows replacement features, dilation features, rotated and far-traveled inclusions, and the occurrence of flows of composition similar to granophyre indicate the existence of magmas of this composition.

The postulated lack of rocks with composition intermediate between gabbro and granophyre led Grout (1918b) to advocate an immiscible separation of granophyre liquid from basaltic magma. Grieg (1927) recognized liquid immiscibility in artificial systems of silicates, but concluded that it is unlikely to operate in the range of magmatic composition. More recently, Holgate revived the hypothesis of liquid immiscibility (1954) to account for the trend of liquid composition in the Skaergaard Intrusion. He based his conclusion on an extension of the two-liquid field from data derived from a study of quartzo-feldspathic reaction rims on siliceous xenoliths enclosed in basic rocks. Holgate's comparison of the liquid trend of the Skaergaard Intrusion with the alkaline rocks of Mull (see Fig. 17) is misleading, however, because a computed line of liquid descent is being compared with a set of rock analyses. The similarity between the Duluth rocks and the Skaergaard rocks is apparent in Figure 16, but equivalent data on the liquid line of descent are not available for Duluth. The trends toward iron-enrichment and later silica-alkali enrichment are apparent for both rock series.

Holgate may have demonstrated the existence of a metastable two-liquid field for xenolithic reaction rims in basaltic liquids, but the slow crystallization with magma movement indicated for the Skaergaard Intrusion and for the Duluth mass seems to preclude the operation of liquid immiscibility to produce granophyre magma. Liquid immiscibility would produce granophyre magma at the wrong time in the sequence,

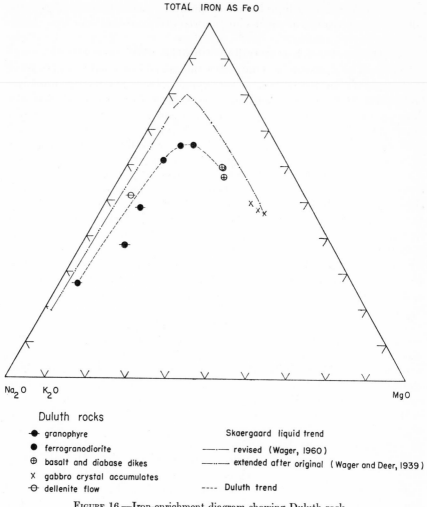

TOTAL IRON AS FeO

Na₂O   K₂O   MgO

Duluth rocks

-●- granophyre   Skaergaard liquid trend

● ferrogranodiorite   ——·—— revised (Wager, 1960)

⊕ basalt and diabase dikes   ——··—— extended after original (Wager and Deer, 1939)

X gabbro crystal accumulates

-⊖- dellenite flow   ---- Duluth trend

FIGURE 16.—Iron-enrichment diagram showing Duluth rock
analyses and Skaergaard liquid trends.

early in the crystallization history, whereas the field data require granophyre to be late, crystallizing after solidification of the major part of
the mass.

Leighton (1954) has reviewed the theories for the origin of granophyre, and concluded that separate injections of magma were necessary
to produce the gabbro-granophyre association of northern Wisconsin.
He showed that the "intermediate rock" of this association is the result of the metasomatism of gabbro by granophyre magma. At Duluth,

there is "intermediate rock" of this origin, which was produced by granophyre acting on the anorthositic gabbro (Grout and Longley, 1935; Goldich, Taylor, and Lucia, 1956). Analyses of contaminated granophyre and of transgressive ferrogranodiorite (Table 15), however, differ appreciably. The granophyre contaminated with more or less assimilated anorthositic gabbro reflects the aluminous and calcic composition of the feldspathic gabbro, but the ferrogranodiorite, although emplaced in the same gabbro, does not show this effect. The average ferrogranodiorite also contains relatively more iron oxides than does the contaminated granophyre.

TABLE 15. COMPARISON OF CHEMICAL ANALYSES
OF "INTERMEDIATE" ROCKS OF DIFFERENT
ORIGIN

	Z	30
SiO_2	51.42	51.97
Al_2O_3	13.31	18.97
Fe_2O_3	4.72	1.98
FeO	9.93	7.07
MgO	2.33	2.67
CaO	6.96	8.60
Na_2O	3.57	3.18
K_2O	1.87	1.43
H_2O+	.87	1.31
H_2O-	.30	.17
CO_2	.03	
TiO_2	2.21	1.90
P_2O_5	.97	.41
MnO	.21	.14
SrO	.03	
	99.73	99.79

Z. Averages of analyses XIII, XIV, XV, Table 11. Transgressive granodiorites.

30. Contaminated granophyre, quarry at 13th Avenue W., Duluth. W. W. Longley, analyst (Grout and Longley, 1935, p. 135).

The complete rock series at Duluth must be emphasized in connection with the origin of granophyre magma. The world-wide occurrence of the gabbro-granophyre association has been pointed out by many writers, and a genetic relationship generally has been postulated. The hypothesis of magmatic differentiation by crystal settling has been depreciated because of the suggested lack of "intermediate" rock, and the idea of "contrasted differentiation" (Nockolds, 1934) has been developed. The present study invalidates these ideas for the Duluth region, and establishes ferrogranodiorite as an intermediate type. The line of liquid descent in the crystallization-differentiation of parental basaltic magma produced differentiates of ferrogranodiorite and granophyre compositions. The variation in composition of the granophyres and evidence of replacement suggest that there is more than a single origin for the granophyre at Duluth. Computations based on the chemical analyses (Table 11) show a range of 16.4–53.4 per cent by weight for Na-feldspar, and 2.4–37.2 per cent for K-feldspar. In my opinion most of the granophyre at Duluth formed from magma. Small amounts of granophyre were also formed by replacement, but the granophyre-forming fluids responsible for the replacement also were derived by the differentiation of the basaltic magma.

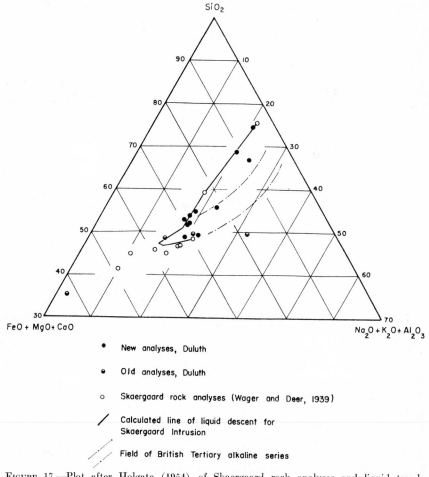

FIGURE 17.—Plot after Holgate (1954) of Skaergaard rock analyses and liquid trend, with Duluth analyses added. Curve of the Skaergaard line of liquid descent reflects the extreme iron-enrichment of this series with the late trend toward enrichment in silica and alkalies. The field of the British Tertiary alkaline series shows the trend from basalt to trachyte.

COMPARISON WITH THE STILLWATER AND SKAERGAARD INTRUSIONS

The layered series of the Duluth Complex shows limited crystallization-differentiation as compared with the Stillwater Complex of Montana or the Skaergaard Intrusion of East Greenland. The Duluth rocks lie between those of the Stillwater and Skaergaard intrusions in the differentiation scheme of basaltic magma.

The Stillwater Complex of Montana (Hess, 1939, 1961) represents only the lowermost crystal accumulates in a sill-like intrusion. About 1700 feet of layered rocks overlie a basal chill zone, and are truncated above by an erosion surface on which lies Paleozoic limestone. The lower layers are ultramafic rocks, chiefly bronzite, pyroxenite, and harzburgite, with minor dunite. Above are norite, gabbro, and anorthosite in irregularly alternating bands. No rocks are exposed at Duluth equivalent to those of the Stillwater Complex, but possibly such occur at depth. The graph (Fig. 17) showing the comparative mineralogy of the Duluth,

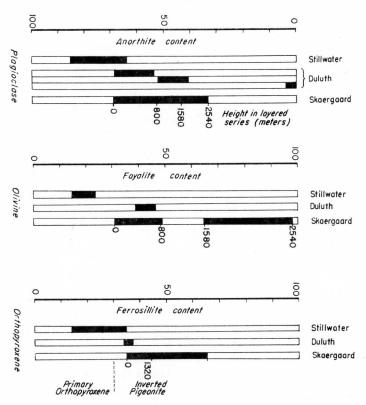

FIGURE 18.—Comparison of ranges in mineral composition for Stillwater, Duluth, and Skaergaard layered intrusions.

TABLE 16. COMPARISON OF CHEMICAL ANALYSES FROM THE SKAERGAARD
INTRUSION AND THE DULUTH COMPLEX

	Skaergaard Intrusion				Duluth Gabbro Complex			
	31	32	33	34	Y	XIV	XVII	XVIII
SiO_2	47.92	52.13	58.81	75.03	49.35	53.78	64.28	73.55
Al_2O_3	18.87	15.87	12.02	13.17	13.75	16.34	14.44	12.05
TiO_2	1.40	1.14	1.26	.31	3.25	1.55	.71	.27
Fe_2O_3	1.18	5.61	5.77	1.56	2.13	4.66	2.83	2.37
FeO	8.65	11.17	9.38	.58	11.11	7.65	3.45	1.09
MnO	.11	.30	.19	.01	.20	.18	.07	.05
MgO	7.82	1.11	.72	.15	5.54	1.31	1.76	.51
CaO	10.46	5.80	5.03	.69	9.09	7.08	1.03	.76
SrO	.04*	.06*	.06*	.02*		.04	.02	.01
Na_2O	2.44	3.63	3.91	4.24	2.72	4.07	4.03	2.85
K_2O	.19	1.38	2.39	3.85	.97	1.76	4.44	5.40
BaO	.00*	.03*	.07*	.17*			.09	.07
P_2O_5	.07	.70	.64*	.02	.53	.54	.15	.05
H_2O+	.41	.86	.21	.28	.87	.65	1.21	.38
H_2O-	.10	.25	.19	.13	.19	.32	.95	.09
CO_2	.06				.03	.03	.02	.16
S	.05*	.05*			.08		.01	.01
	99.77	100.09	100.65*	100.11*	99.81	99.96	99.58	99.67
Less $O \cong S$	−.02	−.02			−.03			
	99.75*	100.07*			99.78			

*Figures from Wager and Mitchell, 1951, added to supplement analyses from Wager and Deer, 1939, analyses retotaled.

31. Average of marginal olivine gabbro 1825, 1724, and 1922 (Wager and Deer, 1939, p. 141, analysis XIIIa; Wager and Mitchell, 1951, Table A, analysis Y).

32. Basic hedenbergite granophyre from the unlayered series at 2700 m, 4137 (1939, p. 114, analysis X; 1951, Table C, analysis XVIII).

33. Hedenbergite granophyre, Brodretoppen, 3047 (1939, p. 210, analysis XXII; 1951, Table D, analysis II).

34. Acid granophyre, sill on Tinden, 3058 (1939, p. 208, analysis XXII; 1951, Table D, analysis V).

Y. Average of basalt dike analyses XXVI, XXVII and XXVIII (Table 14).

XIV. Ferrogranodiorite, M4624. Intrusion in Sec. 28, T.50N., R.14W. R. B. Taylor, analyst.

XVII. Granophyre, M4628. Bardon Peak, Sec. 27, T.49N., R.15W. Irregular mass intruding olivine gabbro. R. B. Taylor, analyst.

XVIII. Granophyric aplitic granite, M3787. Dike intruding dellenite flow, 8th Street at 3rd Avenue W., Duluth. R. B. Taylor, analyst.

Stillwater, and Skaergaard series indicates that the Stillwater Complex lies much "lower" in the differentiation series of a stratiform body.

The Skaergaard Intrusion of East Greenland (Wager and Deer, 1939) has a funnel shape, and about 8800 feet of layered rocks are exposed, ranging from gabbro through ferrogabbro to basic granophyre. A hidden layered series is postulated to be feldspar-rich olivine eucrite. Transgressive granophyre dikes, probably related to the layered series, are the most silicic rock type.

The rock series at Duluth is similar to that of the Skaergaard Complex. For comparison, analyses from the Skaergaard Intrusion and from the Duluth Complex are given in Table 16. The ranges in mineral composition overlap (Fig. 18), but variation in the Duluth rocks is definitely restricted. The similarity of the Skaergaard and Duluth masses is also shown by their position in the stability field of the primary pyroxenes beyond the field of formation of primary orthopyroxene, and in the field of inverted pigeonite (Fig. 18). The transition between these fields lies stratigraphically near the top of the Stillwater Complex and below the exposed sections at Duluth and in the Skaergaard Intrusion.

Wager and Deer (1939, pp. 98–99) defined ferrogabbro as a basic rock with a silica content in the gabbro range, but with olivine containing more than 50 mole per cent of fayalite. Rocks of this composition are not known at Duluth.

The differences in the rock series of the Skaergaard and the Duluth complexes have two fundamental causes. First, the Skaergaard Intrusion is relatively small and crystallized under comparatively stable tectonic conditions. An orderly rock series was produced by uninterrupted crystal fractionation of a single body of magma. The Duluth Gabbro Complex consists of numerous intrusions that differentiated in a region of tectonic instability. Differentiated liquids moved and formed the transgressive bodies. Secondly, the basaltic parent magmas differed in composition. In particular, the Duluth magma had a higher K_2O content. Potassium feldspar appears in some of the upper gabbro; also ferrogranodiorites were formed. The higher potassium content is evident in comparing analyses of the crystal accumulates; the analyzed Duluth rocks contain about 0.5 per cent K_2O, whereas the Skaergaard rocks contain an average of about 0.2 per cent. The partial analysis of the chilled phase of the Duluth layered series (Analysis XXIX, Table 14) and the analyses of the basalt dikes (Table 14) average about 1 per cent K_2O. The basalt dike analyses are perhaps the best indication of the composition of the parent Keweenawan basaltic magma, though there is no certainty that the dikes are not slightly differentiated.

ANORTHOSITIC GABBRO

The feldspathic composition, generally over 75 per cent labradorite, of the anorthositic gabbro makes it unlikely that it represents an undifferentiated liquid. The structure indicates that it was intruded into its present position as a crystal mush containing large blocks of earlier-crystallized gabbros. Perhaps the anorthositic gabbro underwent several periods of partial crystallization in which the first phases to solidify were broken up and intruded by later pushes of the partially crystallized magma. The jumble of blocks of different types of gabbro suggests that the blocks were transported considerable distances from their site of solidification.

The necessary assumption that the anorthositic gabbro represents a crystal accumulate derived from a basaltic parent magma presents a number of questions. The location and shape of the chamber in which the accumulation of feldspar took place, the location of complementary mafic rocks that should accompany such a feldspathic segregation, and the mechanism of separation of the feldspar crystals are all problems for which ready answers are not available. The absence of structures indicating bottom accumulation of crystals, the highly feldspathic composition, and the virtual absence of olivine that characterizes the gabbros of the layered series suggest that the process of differentiation of the anorthositic gabbro was very different from that of the layered series. Some type of differential movement was necessary to separate the feldspar from the liquid; this may have been by crystal floating, but more likely it was accomplished by frictional drag on the crystals during movements of the magma. The expected basic complementary

TABLE 17. COMPARISON OF CHEMICAL ANALYSES OF EXTRUSIVE AND INTRUSIVE ROCKS

	Extrusive Rocks			Intrusive Rocks	
	XXXV	36	37	16	XVIII
SiO_2	64.95	71.12	75.48	66.92	73.55
Al_2O_3	12.58	12.58	12.30	12.73	12.05
Fe_2O_3	4.70	5.20	2.54	4.36	2.37
FeO	4.83	.15	.36	3.93	1.09
MgO	.93	.08	tr	1.66	.51
CaO	2.07	.58	.14	1.20	.76
Na_2O	3.46	2.85	3.43	3.45	2.85
K_2O	4.21	6.19	5.17	3.98	5.40
H_2O+	.54	.22	.24	1.25	.38
H_2O-	.32	.05	.04	.20	.09
CO_2	.03	.18		.02	.16
TiO_2	.82	.45	.21	.69	.27
P_2O_5	.15	.03	.02	.11	.05
MnO	.16	.06	.02	.16	.05
BaO	.12			.06	.07
S	.03			.04	.01
ZrO				.22	
	99.90	99.74	99.95	100.76	99.67
Less $O \cong S$	−.01				
	99.89				

XXXV. Dellenite, M4600. Flow above anorthositic gabbro, 8th Street and 3rd Avenue W. S. S. Goldich and Deane K. Smith, analysts; average of two closely agreeing analyses.

16. Granophyre ("red rock"), NW corner, Sec. 27, T.50N., R.14W. F. F. Grout, analyst (Grout, 1918b, p. 650, No. 25).

36. Rhyolite, flow above Lester River sill. R. W. Perlich, analyst (Schwartz and Sandberg, 1940, Table 1, No. 22).

37. Rhyolite, flow above Endion sill. S. S. Goldich, analyst (Schwartz and Sandberg, 1940, Table 1, No. 7).

XVIII. Aplitic granite, M3787. Dike intruding dellenite flow, 8th Street and 3rd Avenue W. R. B. Taylor, analyst.

rocks may have been cut out by the intrusion of three miles of gabbro of the layered series, but no evidence on their existence is available.

KEWEENAWAN FLOWS

Only three modern chemical analyses of the flows near Duluth are available: a new analysis of the dellenite flow above the gabbro at 8th Street and 3rd Avenue and analyses of two rhyolite flows above the Endion and Lester River sills (Schwartz and Sandberg, 1940). The analysis of the dellenite flow differs considerably from the analyses of the rhyolite flows (Table 17), and suggests that further chemical analyses may reveal a greater diversity among the flows than can be detected by hand specimen identification in the field. The analysis of the dellenite resembles the analysis by Grout (1918b) of the granophyre ("red rock") from the outcrop less than 500 feet to the west. The granophyre intrudes the anorthositic gabbro and the dellenite flow, though the contacts with the flow are covered. The analyses of the rhyolites resemble that of the granite from the small dike that cuts the dellenite flow.

Of significance to the problem of origin of the Duluth Complex is the fact that magmatic liquids existed prior to intrusion of the anorthositic gabbro, and that these magmas ranged in composition from basalt to rhyolite and included intermediate types. The mechanism of differentiation is open to question, as is the position of the hypothetical chamber in which differentiation took place.

REFERENCES AND INDEX

REFERENCES

Aldrich, H. R., 1929, The geology of the Gogebic iron range of Wisconsin: Wis. Geol. Nat. Hist. Survey, Econ. Ser., Bull. 71, 279 p.

Bayley, W. S., 1893, The basic massive rocks of the Lake Superior Region: Jour. Geology, 1893, v. 1, p. 435–456, 587–596, 688–716; 1894, v. 2, p. 814–825; 1895, v. 3, p. 1–20.

———, 1895, The peripheral phases of the great gabbro mass of northeastern Minnesota (abs.): Science, new ser., v. 1, p. 65.

Broderick, T. M., 1917, The relation of the titaniferous magnetites of northeastern Minnesota to the Duluth gabbro: Econ. Geology, v. 12, p. 663–696.

———, 1918, Some features of magnetic surveys of the magnetite deposits of the Duluth gabbro: Econ. Geology, v. 13, p. 35–49.

Brown, G. M., 1957, Pyroxenes from the early and middle stages of fractionation of the Skaergaard Intrusion, East Greenland: Mineralog. Mag., v. 31, p. 511–543.

Elftman, A. H., 1895, Notes upon the bedded and banded structures of the gabbro and upon an area of troctolyte: Minn. Geol. Survey Ann. Rept., v. 23, p. 224–230.

———, 1898, Geology of the Keweenawan area in northeastern Minnesota: Am. Geologist, 1898, v. 21, p. 90–109, 175–188, 1899, v. 22, p. 131–149.

Ernst, W. G., 1960, Diabase-granophyre relations in the Endion sill, Duluth, Minnesota: Jour. Petrology, v. 1, p. 286–303.

Goldich, S. S., A. O. Nier, H. Baadsgaard, J. H. Hoffman, H. W. Krueger, 1961, The Precambrian geology and geochronology of Minnesota: Minn. Geol. Survey Bull. 41, 193 p.

Goldich, S. S., R. B. Taylor, and F. J. Lucia, 1956, Geology of the Enger Tower Area, Guidebook Series, Precambrian of northeastern Minnesota: Geol. Soc. America Guidebook, Minneapolis Meeting, p. 67–90.

Grant, U. S., 1889, Report of geological observations made in northeastern Minnesota during the summer of 1889: Minn. Geol. Survey 17th Annual Report, 215 p.

———, 1899, Contact metamorphism of a basic igneous rock: Geol. Soc. America Bull., v. 11, p. 503–516.

Grieg, J. W., 1927, Immiscibility in silicate melts: Am. Jour. Sci., 5th ser., v. 13, p. 1–44, 133–154.

Grout, F. F., 1918a, The lopolith; an igneous form exemplified by the Duluth gabbro: Am. Jour. Sci., 4th ser., v. 46, p. 516–522.

———, 1918b, A type of igneous differentiation: Jour. Geology, v. 26, p. 626–658.

———, 1918c, Two phase convection in igneous magmas: Jour. Geology, v. 26, p. 481–499.

———, 1918d, A form of multiple rock diagrams: Jour. Geology, v. 26, p. 622–625.

———, 1918e, Internal structures of igneous rocks; their significance and origin; with special reference to the Duluth gabbro: Jour. Geology, v. 26, p. 439–458.

———, 1918f, The pegmatites of the Duluth gabbro: Jour. Geology, v. 26, p. 255–264.

———, 1926, The geology and magnetite deposits of northern St. Louis County, Minnesota: Minn. Geol. Survey Bull. 21.

———, 1933, Duluth rocks and structure: Guidebook 27, 26th Int. Geol. Cong., p. 67–72.

———, 1949–50, The titaniferous magnetites of Minnesota: St. Paul Office of the Commissioner of the Iron Range Resources and Rehabilitation, 117 p.

Grout, F. F., J. W. Gruner, G. M. Schwartz, and G. A. Thiel, 1951, Precambrian stratigraphy of Minnesota: Geol. Soc. America Bull., v. 62, p. 1017–1078.

Grout, F. F., and W. W. Longley, 1935, Relations of anorthosite to granite: Jour. Geology, v. 43, p. 133–141.

Grout, F. F., and G. M. Schwartz, 1939, The geology of the anorthosites of the Minnesota coast of Lake Superior: Minn. Geol. Survey Bull. 28, 119 p.

Harpum, J. R., 1954, The formation of epidote in Tanganyika: Geol. Soc. America Bull., v. 65, p. 1075–1092.

Hess, H. H., 1938, Primary banding in norite and gabbro: Am. Geophys. Union Trans., 19th Ann. Meeting, p. 264–268.

——, 1941, Pyroxenes of common mafic magmas: Am. Mineralogist, v. 26, p. 515–535, 573–594.

——, 1949, Chemical composition and optical properties of common clinopyroxenes: Am. Mineralogist, v. 34, p. 621–666.

——, 1961, Stillwater igneous complex, Montana: a quantitative mineralogical study: Geol. Soc. America Mem. 80, 230 p.

Holgate, N., 1954, The role of liquid immiscibility in liquid petrogenesis: Jour. Geology, v. 62, p. 439–479.

Hotchkiss, W. O., 1923, The Lake Superior geosyncline: Geol. Soc. America Bull., v. 34, p. 669–678.

Irving, R. D., 1883, The copper bearing rocks of Lake Superior: U.S. Geol. Survey Monograph 5, 464 p.

Kennedy, G. C., 1947, Charts for correlation of optical properties with chemical composition of some common rock-forming minerals: Am. Mineralogist, v. 32, p. 561–573.

Kloos, J. H., 1871, Geologische Notizen aus Minnesota: Deut. Geol. Ges. Zeitschr., Band 23, p. 417–448, 648–652; translation, Minn. Geol. Survey Ann. Rept., v. 10, p. 175–200, 1882.

Leighton, M. W., 1954, Petrogenesis of a gabbro-granophyre complex in northern Wisconsin: Geol. Soc. America Bull., v. 65, p. 401–442.

Leith, C. K., R. J. Lund, and A. Leith, 1935, Pre-cambrian rocks of the Lake Superior region: U.S. Geol. Survey Prof. Paper 184, 34 p.

Lucia, F. J., 1954, Igneous geology of the Enger Tower area, Duluth, Minnesota: University of Minnesota, Unpublished M.S. thesis.

Nebel, M. L., 1919, The basal phases of the Duluth gabbro near Gabamichigami Lake, Minnesota, and its contact effects: Econ. Geology, v. 14, p. 367–402.

Nockolds, S. R., 1934, The production of normal rock types by contamination and their bearing on petrogenesis: Geol. Mag., v. 71, p. 31–39.

Sandberg, A. E., 1938, Section across Keweenawan lavas at Duluth: Geol. Soc. America Bull., v. 49, p. 795–830.

Schwartz, G. M., 1944, Tracing the Duluth gabbro contact with a magnetometer: Econ. Geology, v. 39, p. 224–233.

——, 1949, The geology of the Duluth metropolitan area: Minn. Geol. Survey Bull. 33, 136 p.

Schwartz, G. M., and D. M. Davidson, 1952, Geologic setting of the copper-nickel prospect in the Duluth gabbro near Ely, Minnesota: Mining Engineering, p. 699–702.

Schwartz, G. M., and A. E. Sandberg, 1940, Rock series in diabase sills at Duluth, Minnesota: Geol. Soc. America Bull., v. 51, p. 1135–1172.

Taylor, R. B., 1956, The Duluth gabbro complex, Duluth, Minnesota, Guidebook series, Precambrian of Northeastern Minnesota: Geol. Soc. America Guidebook, Minneapolis meeting, p. 42–60.

Van Hise, C. R., and C. K. Leith, 1909, Pre-cambrian geology of North America: U.S. Geol. Survey Bull. 360, 939 p.

——, 1911, Geology of the Lake Superior region: U.S. Geol. Survey Monograph 52, 641 p.

Wadsworth, M. E., 1887, Preliminary description of the peridotites, gabbros, diabases and andesites of Minnesota: Minn. Geol. Survey Bull. 2, 159 p.

Wager, L. R., 1953, Layered intrusions: Meddelelser fra Dansk Forening, Bd. 12, p. 23–349.

——, 1960, The major element variation of the layered series of the Skaergaard Intrusion and a re-estimation of the average composition of the hidden layered series and of the successive residual magmas, Jour. Petrology, v. 1, p. 364–398.

Wager, L. R., and W. A. Deer, 1939, Geological investigations in East Greenland, part III; The petrology of the Skaergaard Intrusion, Kangerdlugssuaq, East Greenland: Meddelelser om Gronland, v. 105, no. 4, 352 p.

Wager, L. R., and R. L. Mitchell, 1951, The distribution of trace elements during strong fractionation of basic magma—a further study of the Skaergaard Intrusion, East Greenland: Geochim. et Cosmochim. Acta, v. 1, p. 129–208.

Winchell, A. N., 1900, Mineralogical and petrographic study of the gabbroid rocks of Minnesota: Am. Geologist, v. 26, p. 151–245, 261–306, 348–388.

Winchell, N. H., 1880, The cupriferous series at Duluth: Minn. Geol. Survey Ann. Rept.,
v. 10, p. 22–26.
———, 1885, The crystalline rocks of Minnesota: Minn. Geol. Survey Ann. Rept., v. 13,
p. 36–40.
———, 1899, Geology of Minnesota: Minn. Geol. Survey Final Rept., v. IV, 630 p.
Winchell, N. H., and H. V. Winchell, 1891, The iron ores of Minnesota: Minn. Geol.
Survey Bull. 6, 430 p.
Winchell, N. H., and U. S. Grant, 1900, The petrographic geology of the crystalline rocks
of Minnesota: Minn. Geol. Survey Final Report, v. 5, 936 p.
Zapffe, C., 1912, Effects of a basic igneous intrusion on a Lake Superior iron-bearing dis-
trict: Econ. Geology, v. 7, p. 145–178.

INDEX

Adamellite, 31
Anorthosite, 9, 12
Anorthositic gabbro: description, 8; contact relations, 9–11; cognate inclusions, 10–11; internal structure, 11; mode, 11; anorthosite, 12; origin, 53–55

Bardon Peak Intrusion: lithology, 28–29; peridotite, 29; chemical analyses, 29
Basalt and microgabbro dikes: Enger Tower, 42; Twin Lakes, 43; chemical analyses, 43; cutting layered series, 44
Biwabik Formation, 4

Chemical analyses: basalt hornfels, 13; pyroxene, 26; gabbroic rocks, 29; ferrogranodiorite, 32; granophyre, 40–42; basalt dikes, 43; extrusive rocks, 49
Contrasted differentiation, 49
Cryptic layering, 2

Duluth Gabbro Complex: location, 1; previous work, 1–2; geologic setting, 4; defined, 6–7; age, 8; anorthositic gabbro, 8–12; layered series, 12–29; Bardon Peak Intrusion, 28–29; peridotite, 29; basic pegmatites, 30–31; ferrogranodiorite, adamellite, syenodiorite, 31–33; ferrogranodiorite-granophyre association, 33–35; granophyre, 36–42; petrology, 45–51; comparison with other areas, 51–53

Endion sill, 7, 36, 46, 55
Enger Tower Intrusion, 34–35

Ferrogranodiorite: occurrence, 31–35; modes, 31; chemical analyses, 32; ferroaugite, 33, 35; dikes, 33; association with granophyre, 33; flow banding, 35; origin, 47–50; iron-enrichment, 48
Fond du Lac Formation, 7

Giant's Range, 4
Glacial deposits, 7
Granophyre: association with ferrogranodiorite, 33; reaction with anorthositic gabbro, 35; lithology, 36; contact relations, 36–37; alteration of basalt, 37; texture, 38–39; albite granophyre, 39; chemical analyses, 40–42; modes, 40; composite dike, 41; origin, 47–50; immiscible liquids, 47–48
Gunflint Iron-Formation, 4

Intermediate rock, 49

Keewatin Greenstone, 4
Kennedy tables, 25
Keweenawan flows, 4, 6, 55
Knife Lake Group, 4

Lake Superior geosyncline, 4
Layered series: description, 12; contact relations, 13–14; internal structure, 14; rhythmic layering, 15; gravitational stratification, 15, 22; petrography, 15–23; modal analyses, 16; mineralogy, 17, 23–28; plagioclase, 25; olivine, 25; pryoxenes, 25–28; Bardon Peak Intrusion, 28; chemical analyses, 29; petrology, 46–47; comparison with Stillwater and Skaergaard intrusions, 51–53; parent magma, 53
Leitz universal stage, 25
Lester River sill, 55

North Shore Volcanic Group: description, 6; contacts with Duluth Complex, 9, 14; chemical analyses, 54

Olivine: anorthositic gabbro, 12; layered series, 17, 25

Parent magma, 53
Pegmatites: basic, 31; in granophyre, 36
Peridotite, 29
Petrology: problems, 45; layered series, 46–47; transgressive ferrogranodiorite and granophyre, 47–50; comparison with Stillwater and Skaergaard intrusions, 51–53; anorthositic gabbro, 53–55; Keweenawan flows, 55
Plagioclase: anorthositic gabbro, 12; layered series, 17, 25; ferrogranodiorite, 32–35; granophyre, 35
Pleistocene deposits, 7
Precambrian history, 4, 8, 45–46
Puckwunge Formation, 6
Pyroxene: anorthositic gabbro, 12; layered series, 17, 25–28; ferrogranodiorite, 33, 35; basalt dikes, 43